# Revolt of the Idiots:
## a Story

# Revolt of the Idiots:
# a Story

Burton Blatt

**EXCEPTIONAL PRESS**
Box 188, Glen Ridge, New Jersey

EXCEPTIONAL PRESS EDITORIAL OFFICE
BOX 344
SAN JUAN CAPISTRANO, CA. 92675
(714) 493-8405

Jacket and frontispiece illustrations by Judith Cohen.

ISBN 0-914420-58-6

Printed in the United States of America

10 9 8 7 6 5 4 3 2 1

Dedicated to our sons:
Eddie, Steve, and Mike.
They enrich our lives.

# PROLOGUE

This is a work of fiction. But, I have wondered, what does that mean? Is fiction always more untrue than that self-serving segment of non-fiction which seeks to justify and, in the process, only deludes? And, for those who only fantasize, how are their worlds less real than the world as you see it—or I? Again, what is fiction? Can it be what one writes to illuminate the obvious, or is it the stuff that describes the indescribable?

In light of the above, it may now be claimed that, with the exception of several friends, distinguished colleagues, and well-known state schools whose names are mentioned in this story, all characters, places, and events are fictitious. Further, even in those instances where live people and places are part of the story's substance, everything related to their involvements are, similarly, creations of the writer's imagination. The reader has been advised.

Although this is only a story, the fact remains that I have spent some time studying state institutions. While the story should be considered as fictional, nevertheless, I have attempted to describe institutional life, and I discuss genuine problems confronting our society. Undoubtedly, there will be readers who will find parts of this story to be unbelievable. But that is just the point: Were the world different, could we better appreciate the "unbelievable"?

Several of the conversations and talks on these pages are approximate replays of past encounters between real people attempting to deal with concrete issues. Most of these, much of my verse and discussions, and some historical documentation are distinguished by different type faces than used here, to permit those readers primarily interested in the story itself to disregard what may be, to them, disconcerting intrusions. Obviously, the reader is always the best judge of what to read, what to scan, and what to ignore. Derrick TePaske's and Don Heiny's photographs are recent products of their visits to actual state institutions and other places.

Thus, while the story is wholly fictional, I tried throughout to write the truth as I understand truth. For, although it has been said that truth is stranger than fiction, I can also believe that fiction may best portray certain strange truths.

May, 1976                                                            Burton Blatt

# Contents

# Revolt of the Idiots:
## a Story

The first photo essay is how it usually is; the second, how it can be.
The first group illustrates institutional settings; the second, that of the community sheltered workshop.


Photo essay on page 120: Photographer Derrick Te Paske.
Photo essay on page 247: Photographer Don Heiny.

# Chapter 1

## Fathers

There was a man named Adam Mack. He was tall, with a fair complexion, solid features, straight lines. He stood erect, but not as a rock—like a piece of more pliable stuff, receptive. He was a rough and sometimes crude man, but a gentle man, who lived at The New Hope State School. This story tells of Adam's unfolding, the uprising he led at New Hope, what he learned, what men and women learn while seeking maturity and a destiny. For if Adam had not grasped the rod, the future surely would have brought a fate worse than the snake bite, worse than destruction; it would have brought complete and final disillusionment. Along with the many who were involved, I too learned—both from the experience and in the process of setting it down on paper.

And who am I? I am someone who is trying to understand the process of artistic creation. I am trying to unravel the relationship between art and one's awakening. It has something there that is a clue to human development. I am also an observer, a writer; more correctly, one who attempts to write, an escapist; better, one who is trying to escape, and—at the moment—a recently employed, now unemployed, attendant at the Libertyville State School. Once I, too, was at New Hope. As they say in the central office, my career, my ladder to achievement in mental health, began as an attendant at New Hope. I followed Adam Mack and his cohorts from the beginning. The end of this book does not complete the story. The end is merely a technical break designed to provide the opportunity to disseminate a part of the story that is past history.

And what of the story? It is about Adam Mack, who lived for many years as an inmate at New Hope State School, a public institution for what commonwealth laws still refer to as "mental defectives." It is about Mike Edward, a professor of education at the university, who was Adam's teacher, as Adam later became his. It is about Cy Bernard, another professor, who learned that dangerous ideas lead to action; the world of the mind, if it is fertile, cannot be contained in the mind; eventually, it must find expression.

This story is about yearnings, the dreams that humans have, the hopes that we, at least once in our lives, expect to become reality—if we live long enough, or pray hard enough, or become lucky enough. This story is about the inmates and those who controlled them, and about those who controlled those who controlled them. It is about Zelman Gabler, who knew that they who own the language own everything, who would lead battles to free any involuntary inmate of the state school.

It is also about me, the storyteller, who saw it all live and heard it all live, or saw a piece and heard a bit, and—never mind how—wrote it down on paper so that it could be put together, however crudely, for other people to understand, for the sake of history, and for those who participated.

Now, let me tell you the story, from the middle, to the beginning, to this day. Let me share with you what really occurred in that modern Draconian culture the department called New Hope State School.

The sun oozed through cracks and torn shade, warm and pleasing; even the drifting dust appealed to Adam's mind's eye. The cobwebs left. Another day, neither good nor bad. At least you may count on it! Better for him than for most here.

The bed felt nice, a good smell, comfortable, same bed, same blanket, same spot, like an old shoe—a good friend. Nine years, one pillow, familiar dust, and sun. Home!

He had known a lot, and much of that a lot worse than here.

He used to talk about those foster homes that grabbed him after his own mother and father died. How many were there—five, eight, ten? I do not think he remembered them all. But he remembered the cold, and the hunger, and the beatings. He remembered the sweet-evil smiles, the darting eyes of the now-parents and their real children, the greedy, grasping, tearing apart of those money envelopes containing his right to remain and be fed and be given a real home life. He remembered the all-important check from social services, the "everything" check. He remembered the waiting and then the agony of the county inspection. Howdyado. Very good. Wonderful boy. Great kid.

Treat him as our own. Ole buddy, pal, we'll have a catch after dinner
—ice cream tonight! And he remembered how it really was all the
other times, with every mom and pop. He remembered so well that he
was glad to be sent to the state school—after it was all explained to
him. And, if he had to admit it, he was never as unhappy at New Hope
as in those awful places and with those awful moms and pops.

---

If I could be a special man, pasted to
    the wall
And make myself appear to go, or change to
    short or tall
If I could hide behind the leaves, or high atop a tree
Where I would gaze and stare at you, but me you
    couldn't see
If I could hide within the cracks, between the clouds,
    on top of air
Then, like the angels in God's land, I'd travel here,
    there, anywhere
If I could spend some time with you, a day, a
    month, a year
So I might learn what makes you laugh, or need
    to shed a tear
If I could do these things I say, and yet not
    trade my soul
Then I would learn more of your world, and write
    this story whole
If I could do what demons do, and still remain alive
I'd hitch my senses to the wind, and take it for
    a drive
If I could get into your heads, or sit inside
    your ears
This story I'm about to write might ring more
    straight and clear
But knowing what I know of life, I know I ask
    too much
For what we mortals bring to art are merely sights,
    and sounds, and touch
And so I'll write this story plain, as any
    other history
Without a devil's sense, or angels' help,
    without the mystery.

# "General Notes"

1. *I had known worse! New Hope State School—a name, not a place, old hope but no joke; I attend to things among the many: 2300 patients too many; 800 staff too many; 600 acres, a lot of acres too many.*

2. *Created: 1907*
   *Capital assets: $30,000,000*
   *Material: Too many   ("Material": ma-têr'i-al, commonwealth syn-onym for inmate, patient, or resident)*
   *Items: Too many   ("Item": ī-tam, commonwealth synonym for state employee but usually refers to attend-ants and other nonprofessionals)*
   *But O.K.,*
   *Adam's happy.*
   *So am I.*

3. *New Hope State School, another among the many. Not famous, not infamous, not well known, not unknown, not the model, more the mode.*

*Never chosen, yet never unchosen, in truth or untruth, never in-cluded on lists that expose and demand that we reform and restore, vitalize and renew, never listed among such places as:*

*Partlow State School*
*Kentucky Training Home*
*Forest Haven Training School*
*Belchertown State School*
*Fairbault State School*
*Willowbrook State School*
*Pennhurst State School*
*Petersburg Training School*
   *Etc. etc., etc.,*
*And on and on and on.*

*But neither included in this litany: Praise be to those who serve man well.*

*And praise:*
*Arkansas Children's Colony*
*Seaside Regional Center*
*that decent Training and Research Center*
      *and Regional Centers*
      *and Hostels*
      *and Normalization*
      *and Humanization*

How's it going, Adam?
   O.K., O.K., O.K.
That's the boy, Adam.
   O.K., O.K.
Atta boy, Adam.
   O.K.
Happy day, Adam.
   It's a day.
Get a move.
Shouldn't you know?
Wash your face.
Wipe your nose.
Say your prayers.
C'mon let's go.
Another day.

Our Father, we have no fathers, but we are Your sons. And if You forsake us, there will be nothing. So be our Father.

Where you headin', Adam?
   New job today.
That's real good, Adam.
Gonna work, Adam?
Then ya gotta move, Adam.
Yes, by God, Adam, we'll have fun today.

     *Binet Hall:*
     Built: 1907
     Material: 114
     Items: 21
     This shift: 4
     Neat as a pin,
     Clean as a whistle.

And you are all good-hearted men,
Upright men.
And you fear the Lord,
Shun evil.
The sons of God,
Saved.
Amen.

Praise to those who keep His commandments, who will not try His patience, who walk in His path, who love Him, who fear Him, who obey, praise, praise, praise.

     Cursed be he who mocks Him and His servants,
     Who mocks the commonwealth,

The superintendent,
The governor,
The lieutenant governor,
Cursed be he; cursed be they.

Adam, Adam,
Saw you steal the cake.
Don't you know the sign says,
"Ask, but don't take"?
Oh, you thieving Adam,
I think you better stop.
Gotta, by God I gotta, tell your Mom and Pop.
It's all right, Adam.
You know not what you do.
Your Mom and Pop will teach you:
Don't steal,
Or else you're through!
Now, you know what not to do!

Thank you, Mom. Thank you, Pop. Thank the Lord. Saved from the gate, and from my brothers, who would surely stone me, that I would die.

Good, it's settled.
Let's get to work.
Lots to do,
Busy, busy, jerks—ha, ha, ha.
C'mon Adam, c'mon Fred,
Mom and Pop want that bread,
Else you're dead—ha, ha, ha.

The small, fat lips slowly part
A drop of sweat, a piece of snot
The mouth extends from ear to ear
The belly bursts, as filled with beer
Pop's facile mole looked just like hers
But Liz Taylor's a beauty, and he's a cur
Under her mark is a face with class
And, around that brute's is a misplaced ass.

Adam Mack,
No middle name,
Caucasian,
Age: 27.
Medium and medium,

No distiguishing marks,
But I.Q.: 63.

Adam's not distinguished, but he did not have bad marks, except in school, when he went to school, long ago, for not too long, when the world was less worn, but Adam more than he will be.

Long ago, when just a babe,
Far back in time, and place, and hope,
He had a Mom and a Dad,
And they had a son,
Father, I have no father.
"Father, I have no mother."
"All together now: Father, we have no Father."

But ages ago, before m.r., before retard, before special, before opportunity knocked, before Mom and Dad went—before this god-damned Pop—before he was so goddamned special, he was a human being.

"Before that, we were a family,
And there were friends and cousins,
Fights and Saturdays free,
Five shorts at the movie,
A new comic thrown in.
And, we had a house,
Our own home."

And he remembered:

Palm Sunday, 1955
"Hurry Adam, we'll be late for church."
"Gee, the car looks great, Dad."
"Not bad for an old buggy."
"Nancy, don't run, you'll fall and tear your clothes."

Mom always worried about Nancy's clothes. What about her skin and knees? Hail and hallelujah! Boy, I'm starved.
"O.K. Son, let's splurge this time. All my children who want Pancake Cottage raise hands. The hands have it!"
"Don, these children will be spoiled forever."
No, they won't!
History is the basic science. From history flows more than knowl-edge, more than prescription, more than how it was: how we might try to make it become. And, what is that old adage? The one thing we learn from history is that we do not learn from history. Yet, it is the

basic science. Physics is a history. Mathematics is a history. Chemistry is a history. Humans have two unique gifts: language and creativity. The way we express history is the ultimate utilization of those gifts. If there were but a poet with such talents and the interest to record Adam's history, much could be revealed; possibly, great discoveries would be made.

Once the priests, the teachers, the parents, and the movies—especially the movies—told him the world will be good, always; will be better, better even than now. Be a good boy. Love God. Love Mom and Dad.

And now, the liars tell him, keep your nose clean, Adam. Work hard, worker boy. Learn, listen, obey. And he heard the lies about today, about tomorrow. And he tried to believe.

What else does a man have? A faith, a dream of bygone days. And things that never were but should have been, would have been, had He kept us. Had He not forsaken us. Father, we are not your children until we are delivered, here on earth.

How did it all happen, Adam? One day you have a family—Mom, Dad, Nancy, and Shawn. Things are going well. Dad has a steady job at the machine shop on Winchester Avenue. Mom is at home, except for Friday and Saturday nights when she works as a waitress at the Tivoli Restaurant. One day there's a family and the next brings three new orphans to the state. Dad had gone to the restaurant to pick up Mom. As usual while Dad waited he talked with Angelo, the bartender. Suddenly, a man who had been drinking at the bar pulled out a gun and shot Dad and Angelo dead. Mom came running. She was killed. Before it ended, two other people were hit, one—Albert Vallo—dying in the ambulance on the way to the hospital. Authorities never did learn why Howard Treck killed these people, none of whom he knew. And Adam never did learn why he was sent to New Hope, except that he had been a wild kind of kid in school and was, eventually, placed in the special class for the retarded. And except that Aunt Flo and Uncle Joe just couldn't take the kids. Little Nancy and Shawn were placed in foster homes and Adam was sent to New Hope. But, in plain truth, he never did learn why he was sent to New Hope. One day you have everything, the next day nothing.

# Chapter 2

## Boast Not of Tomorrow

Father, who may be in heaven, be there. And be in J. E. Wallace Wallin Hall. Be with the patients. Be with Mr. Johnson, the matron. Matron? Where else but at New Hope?

> Strange place, with Mr. Matrons,
> Where people are material,
> And items,
> Where it's hard to get in,
> But who wants to?
> Yet harder to get out,
> Though everybody needs to.

*8/3/72   Author's Diary*

## "An Economics Lesson"

New York State: 1972
Syracuse State School: Built in 1854
Tear down and rebuild
Except, make it bigger by three times
$3 \times 250 = 750$
$\$25,000,000 = \$33,333$ per bed.

Hello, Mr. Johnson.
    Howdyado, howdyado, howdyado.

I'm Adam, the new worker boy.
Yes I know; sure I know; you bet I know.
Thank you, Mr. Johnson; you're very kind.
You're darn tootin' I am; O.K., let's go!

Wallin Hall. If he knew of this designation, would he rest in peace? What would that old curmudgeon—so frail, yet so incredibly strong, that honest and decisive man—make of Wallin Hall, his namesake? Filth, disorder, vomit, noise, screams, cankers and other sores, disease, oblivion—what words would he have? After all, words are abstractions. Poets extend the privilege, and—just maybe—the state even more.

Wallin Hall. A chronic care building, not a cesspool? A facility of the commonwealth, not an abomination reflecting all that is evil in our culture? A facet of New Hope's continuum-of-care concept, not a bottomless pit for the unloved and unwanted? A unit named to honor the memory of that great pioneer special educator, J. E. Wallace Wallin (truly a giant, ask the professors): zealous advocate for children with special needs, diagnostician, educator, public administrator, scholar, humanitarian.

How would Wallin describe Wallin Hall? How would:
J. M. G. Itard
E. Seguin
S. G. Howe
C. Bernstein
M. Montessori
D. L. Dix[1]

How would:
S. A. Kirk
S. B. Sarason
E. A. Doll
I. I. Goldberg
R. H. Hungerford
M. M. Klaber
J. Tizard
E. F. Zigler
M. N. Neuber

How would:
F. F. Finn
W. Wolfensberger
G. Dybwad

[1] To uninformed readers, take my word that these folks must be listed, or look them up and make your judgments. For, dare I tell this story and not record these names?

F. J. Menolascino
B. Nirje
or:
Moses
Abraham Lincoln
Helen Keller
Mohandas Gandhi
And how will you describe Wallin Hall?

shit
vomit
shrieks
blood
pus
torture

---

*As we have been told in Deuteronomy, and it came to pass, the Lord saw we did not harken unto His voice, and we did not obey His commandments. And, because we were not righteous, He ceased to bless us. And, because we sinned against God, He cursed us.*

*We are cursed in the city,*
*and in the field.*
*As is the fruits of our bodies,*
*and our lands.*
*We are cursed when we come in,*
*and when we go out.*
*We are smitten with consumption,*
*and with fear,*
*with inflammation,*
*and with fiery heat,*
*with drought,*
*and with mildew.*
*The Lord has made the rain of our land*
*powder and dust—until we are destroyed.*
*He smites us with the boil of Egypt,*
*with the scab,*
*the itch,*
*with madness,*
*and with blindness.*
*We are oppressed and robbed always,*
*And there are none to save us.*

*Other men lie with our wives.*
*Others live in our houses.*
*Others eat our fruit.*
*Others take our children.*
*We plant vineyards, but neither may we*
*drink the wine nor eat the grapes.*
*We beget sons and daughters, but they*
*are not ours.*
*All the trees and the fruit of our land are*
*possessed by the locust.*
*And, we too.*
*The Lord created man,*
*And man created institutions,*
*And because man so sinned against God,*
*He created Wallin Hall,*
*Whose windows open to nothing,*
*A time for oblivion.*

---

*8/11/72   Author's Diary*

## "More on Economics"

In New York State—in any state?—we continue to construct residential facilities at costs from $30,000 to $60,000 *per bed.* Further, to improve these cesspools, to reform them in the ways government knows how to reform, operating costs may exceed $50 per day per resident—sometimes a good deal more. And we continue to build more and more institutions, some large and some small, medically oriented or educationally oriented, some better and some worse. But, all—*all, all, all*—inferior to other living places in profound ways, in subtle ways, in gross ways, in ways we understand, and in ways yet to be revealed.

And all the while, community-program concepts of normalization and integration, and the range of viable alternatives to institutionalization exist as figments of our hopes, elaborate products of our imagination. All the while, there have not been—and there are not today— functional alternatives to institutionalization. *That* is the no-option no-other-way, ideological as well as physical monolith which Americans term mental health; a reality which is—as often as it is not— injurious to mental health, physical health, and spiritual health.

Days of darkness, nights for death,
As in the days of Job, these are our days.
For this is the day I wished not to have been born.
This is the day as dark as our night.
Yet, we are the people who fear not death,
For we are dead,
Who despair not the darkness,
For we are comforted by its anonymity,
Who died in the womb,
And perished at birth,
And during each succeeding moment,
From then to now.

And the nothingness—nowhere times everywhere—continued, in spite of the best efforts of man and his laws, in spite of Judge Johnson, who ruled in federal court that not only do the mentally retarded have a right to treatment but they also have a right to such treatment in the "least restricted setting necessary for habilitation."

I am a man-child,
   yet neither either.
I am dead,
   yet live to observe and report.
I am called "brainless,"
   yet must lead you who have everything.
And this brainless, dead, man-child observes that:
In the name of science, we kill and plunder.
In the name of man, we justify the murder
   of our brothers.
In the name of God, we certify it all as
   His Will Be Done.

And it came to pass that Adam worked, from early morning until long past such time as one would have thought reasonable. He mopped the day room floor, then the dormitory floor. He changed linens soiled yellow by piss and vomit and black and brown by shit. He mopped again and then picked up the fire hose to wash down the hulking masses of human debris. "Clean washdown fore and aft; shipshape; Adam, anything moves, you hose." He would dress a resident, turn away for a moment; then, clothes would be torn off, a nude glob, grinning and uttering sounds that no human being could possibly produce. "Mop the floor, Adam. Then dress Charlie again."

He worked and observed and thought about things, about the residents—poor, sick, and disgusting—about the attendants, about the matron, and about himself; and, for the first time in ages, about his humanity, his feelings, his life—his, his, *his*!

The days and the nights passed, one to the next, a sameness within a constellation of different tasks—some burdensome, some pleasant. He enjoyed the morning and afternoon coffee breaks, sitting at a table with a few attendants—each a real man. And, as the tall tales, gossip, and jokes were exchanged, he would feel warm—good warm—and he would know that this was the life. Big, rawboned young men, still with the manner and look of the country; black young men, trying to find a way to make it; others—all ages and appearances—trying to find a way to hold on; and the old ones, the veterans of state schools and state hospitals, the union leaders, the stabilizers of the system, the pops and their moms—these were his "friends," the guys he could count on. And, it all seemed so real and so true, especially at coffee break.

He heard stories about the frontier, stories passed on and on and on from father to child, stories about live and dead Indians, wild animals, cold winters, pioneers, Bunyan and Boone, and others not in the books but in the hearts of countless generations of local worshippers.

He heard stories of the plantations and the ghettos and, in spite of himself and the bad feelings he sometimes had about blacks, he loved those stories. He would be almost hypnotized as he listened to the descriptions of hardships and poverty beyond imagination; yet even as the plot seemed to become most desperate, rich and beautiful laughter would emerge, both from the storyteller and, magically, from the characters in the tale.

He heard hard-luck and no-luck stories. These made him sad, made him wonder about the cosmos, even though he did not then know the word and, if he did, might not then have understood its meaning.

And he heard from the pops, the regulars, stories of the old days, when things were different, when the world was better. And, even he would laugh at the jokes and incidents stored in lifetimes devoted to building such collections.

He heard history—raw, slanted, semiliterate, and idiosyncratic, but genuine history—of institutions and of those who keep them. He was fascinated.

And so, with mixtures of pain and pleasure, good and bad feelings, he did the job, drank the coffee, and learned the rules—two sets. First, those for the regular inmate: in the special world of institutions, one learns the rules only by breaking them, and is happy if he's not depressed, with full control when not unhinged, for he's alive just because he's not dead but dead while he lives.

He also learned the rules for the worker boy. They were simple and clear; do as you are told, be neat, do as you are told, be honest, do as you are told, be cheerful, do as you are told, work hard, do as you are told, and *do as you are told.*

He learned a regularity of the institution that is hardly ever a regularity anywhere but in the institution: when you think about things, how they should be and how they are, and you shrug your shoulders, as when those outside want to say, "That's the way it is," but you mean "That's the way it's awful."

In spite of the rules and in spite of the work, Adam found that it was better to work than to be idle, better to move about than to sit, better to leave Binet Hall, where he lived, than remain there too long, choose whether to leave or not to leave, better to have such freedom than not to. Most of all, it was better to live in Binet Hall than in Wallin, where he worked.

Wallin Hall was a special hell and, if he could then, Adam might have described it this way:

> Urine, trickling down naked flesh,
> Running on smooth terrazzo,
> Streams of hot piss inching toward the center,
> As gravity pulls the wicked sticky yellow,
> From one hole to another,
> Leaving its markers here and there,
> Straight lines of dried piss,
> Amid islands of old, old shit,
> As attendants in gleaming white,
> Step carefully to avoid the inmates,
> While bravely they navigate through the oozing slime,
> Gleaming white and untouched by human hands.

And the noises Adam had to hear each day were the noises of:

> Words that have no meaning,
> Sounds that do,
> Jabber, jabber, and yahoos,
> The harpies will getcha,
> If you're in this school.

And the vacuums that hollowed his life were the vacuums of:

> Not real lives that move and mouth,
> With skin so smooth and eyes near-blue,
> And hair that's thick and red or white,
> Almost perfect, almost real,
> Look through those eyes that look through you,
> Those eyes that see through you to walls,
> Through walls to walls through walls,
> To you through you to finiteness,
> To the end.

Adam observed and learned as he viewed those lives and knew their plight, and saw that to see all is not to see, and to live all is not to love.

> Without guile or shame or layers of muck,
> He will teach us with trust and grace,
> That there is also terror to no end,
> And nothing to infinity.
>
> Together, inching to the puzzle,
> We observed the shuffles, sought out the eyes,
> Grasped some arms, embraced the flesh,
> And found our answer.
>
> They move and speak,
> And look like man,
> So damned real,
> Creatures, so man-damned.

And he saw all those who walk with Moloch and he worried with them, for:

> When you walk with Moloch you pay,
> More than you have,
> You pay more than you know,
> Less than he wants.
>
> When you walk with Moloch you're with the devil,
> Beelzebub!
> Harpies,
> Yahoos.
>
> Tread with care!
> Step in slime, and you slip,
> And you're trapped,
> Engulfed.
>
> Avoid state schools,
> And state hospitals,
> And state humanitarians,
> And the state!
>
> Each can make you wish for Moloch,
> As each seeks to prove its goodness,
> As each confirms the evil one,
> And their gifts to his design.
> And their murder of the kindest Brownie!

So Adam—the worker, the resident, the servant of the state, of the institution, of the Monolith—learned not to feel too much or think too much. He taught himself not to boast or guess what tomorrow might bring—else what little luck he had could leave him. It wasn't even that he had lost hope, but more that he hadn't known it, or thought about it, for many years. His was the "disease" of someone who not only compromised his humanity but also failed to perceive it as compromised.

This child of the state had yet to learn what most rich men fail to learn and what makes wise men wise:

> Tomorrow
> The lament of the idle and the anxious
> The portent of unfulfilled hopes
> The look forward to sameness
>
> Tomorrow, while one's life decays
> Tomorrow, as people suffer
> Tomorrow, in a mad civilization
> Tomorrow, through a distorted today
>
> The wind, life, and time move on
> As elements and people pass through
> We are all entwined in an unfathomable cosmic scene
> And, as players everywhere, we learn our roles
>
> By living the parts
> As each attempts to contribute
> To a grander design
> Than the evil one.

He had yet to know of those matters. But, when he was later "told" that Mike Edward owned him, his reply was, "If that's true, better he than the state!"

# Chapter 3

## Victims and Victimizers

Why was I there? To learn how to think better and so to write better. I want to create through my words, and this place gives me the time to think and the stuff to observe. What stuff? The only stuff that matters—people. The only stuff central to thought; the only stuff that thinks back.

Why this place? Who is more different than the different? Who is more unique than the one-of-a-kind? In a world where the average guy has a head circumference of twenty inches, who is more original than the man whose head is two-thirds the size? The craziness of this place and the subnormality of its inhabitants may well contain the elements for creating new thoughts, or new themes on old thoughts, or new words, or new plays on old words.

Men have found their God or themselves in such places; I sought to discover my mind amid these supposed mindless. I pray to become fluent, and I wagered a period of my development that, here among the incoherent, the flow of imagination, dreams, and ideas to words would receive encouragement to create something, to resist the inclination not to write to avoid being a bad writer.

In the back ward,
    Who is the victim
    And who is the victimizer?
Each is; all are.
    Who is dehumanized?
    Who are the cruel

And what is cruelty?
Each is; all are; everything.

In any institution, if there is a back ward, can there be anything *but* a back ward? As the back ward continues to exist, are all people chronic victims and pervasive victimizers? In that institution, is not the term "back ward" a synonym for "institution?"

He who victimizes others
Is the victim
Of his inevitable dehumanization.
As he who is dehumanized
Must contribute
To the dehumanization of others.

All men, willing or unwilling, knowing or unknowing, are victimized during the trials of living as their debasements and agonies victimize other men.

Our way of living
Tests each man's humanity
Assaults it
And sometimes is his conqueror.
As each man contributes
To our way of living
To his own dehumanization
To the dehumanization of all others.
As each man is his own
Victim
And victimizer.

*9/4/72   Author's Diary*

## "Adam's Thoughts This Day, as Later Reported by Him to Writer, and Recorded Here in Writer's Words"

"God, it really does stink here. I thought I'd be used to it by this time. But I'm not, especially after a long walk across fields, then coming in this place. A good thing these 'low grades' can't think. They probably don't even smell all of this shit. If you have to live here, hope you're a 'low grade.' But, I can't feel good about the place. It smells so bad, and the attendants really yell at the low grades. And, once in awhile, they really beat on them.

**20**

"Usually, though, the attendants treat them pretty good. These guys have a hell of a job. I know; I work my ass off too. And what can you do with these animals? If I'm not fast, one of these bastards will piss all over me. They vomit, and drool, and shit, and they don't care if it's on you or them. Look at that stupid bastard, sucking the pus from Joe Collucci's sore arm. I had better put a stop to that; Mr. J. wouldn't like it. 'Move the ef over, you dumb bastard. Hurry up or I'll take this mop and bash it over your head.' Would I really do that? Bet your sweet ass, if I had to. Naw, I wouldn't really hurt one of these—what does Mr. J. call them?—vegetables. I wonder why he calls them that? It doesn't really make much sense."

---

*9/6/72  Author's Diary*

# "Brothers and Strangers"

*The most beautiful words in our testament admonish us not to wrong a stranger, for we were strangers in the land of Egypt. These words are beautiful, not in the morphological sense—for alone they are no more than ordinary words—but in their pristine elemental truth concerning man, his needs, and his anxieties.*

*Each must live alone, must be consumed or learn to deal with his being and his mortality. Each man must find his way to fight the perils, ignore the demons, sustain a personal meaning of living and his share and place in it.*

*In the intimate sense, each man is a stranger to all mankind. In the social sense, we risk being total strangers, globally estranged. In the intimate sense, each man must face the omnipotent alone and resourceless. In the social sense, some find their brothers and, thus, find their strength and their contentment.*

*What responsibility do I have for you and you for me? Am I my brother's keeper, and are all men my brothers? And, if all men are my brothers, is there more than one meaning to the word "brother"?*

*What are the links between us, between your life and mine, your past and my future? What are our ties from the genetic pool, the metaphysical relationship, the human reality and mutuality?*

*Is each man a responsibility of all men, and is each man responsible for all men? Am I my brother's keeper, and are all men my brothers? I know I am, and they are. We are intertwined as one; and, as one, each man must pursue his individuality and unique destiny.*

*And, as one, when my brother suffers, I suffer. And, as one, until* the world is righted for all people, no one is safe, neither you, nor I, nor our progeny. And, as one, each man is part of all men, as all mankind is the sum and effects of each man. My issue, my brothers, and I are all mankind.

Adam, Adam, join your brothers,
Remove the stink,
    the shit,
    the vomit,
    the pus,
    the piss,
    the blows,
    the screams,
    the inhumaneness,
Against these, your brothers.

Converge with others,
And disperse,
And change the world.

Men of like hearts come together.
Share your faith and thoughts.
Tell of the things you have seen,
The wounds you have healed,
The hurts you have caused,
The sores you let fester.

Men of strong minds, your trust entwined,
Recite those histories only you may know.
Ponder theologies that resist extinction.
And prepare your briefs,
Your demands,
For humanity.

Men of fire and fury,
And men of gentleness,
Restore to each other,
Strength and love,
And wisdom.
Then disperse,
And change the world.

———————————————

# Chapter 4

## Fragments From a Diary: 2/70 to 6/72

I see a thigh,
And then the eyes.
The body twists,
The lips unkissed.
The hand will move. "Who's that dame?"
A naked being without a name!
She comes to us, to live then die.
She once stood straight; and now she lies.
It moves its gums!
We say, "Ho hum,"
Then sit and wait,
Resigned to fate.
We watch those holes that once were eyes.
We see the mouth that can't tell lies.
The flesh is red, as dipped in blood.
The matter smells from shit and crud.
And, all the while, the good state smiles.
But the good state's smiles are stuffed with bile.
And, all the while, the people die,
For all those smiles are guile and lies.
But this is truth, or I hope to die.

**2/2/70**

What am I doing here? What do I do here? Is this reality? Well, one day on the job and I'm still employed, a servant of the commonwealth, at $198.57 before deductions every second Thursday. Didn't Pennington say that I must work at living? I must seek that life around me that is now mysterious. I must find reality if I'm ever to write. I must find it so that I can deal with it. Didn't she say that artists distort reality to create reality? What does one do when the reality doesn't need artistic distortion, when distortion is part of the natural fabric, when distortion is reality? Is that special reality, then, a creation of art or a work of madness? Here I am, Pennington. Help!

*3/9/70*

The commonwealth tells me that my primary responsibility is to the building, the patients, the department of mental health. Yet, I tell myself that my true obligation is to my poetry, my art, my creations. Can we both be correct? Why do I write: for fame, wealth, the fulfillment of lovely dreams? Or, maybe, as Gabler wrote in his new book, I've learned that to control language is to control everything important? I must meet that man, so close, yet far away. I must talk with him about anarchy, language, and freedom. I must also spend more time analyzing myself and my motives and my priorities.

*3/13/70*

The department of mental health labels the inmate "material"; and, now, the department responsible for its aged clients identifies these people as "inventory." Yet, state officials are usually offended whenever governmental "welfare" is judged as dehumanizing.

*4/2/70*

I had a fascinating experience with Elbie Cassel today, a resident I delivered" to Dr. Weitman, the school's dentist. While we were waiting for the doc to see Elbie, we got to talking. I've been wanting to speak with Elbie since I heard about him soon after I first came to New Hope. He's known as an idiot savant, literally a "brilliant defective." He's a "low grade" (can't take care of himself, like going to the dentist alone), yet he can do all sorts of other things. He's what they call a "calendar calculator"; he can tell you the day of the week of any date since Christ to the next millennium. He can; I tested him. Also knows almost the exact time of the day without consulting a watch. When I asked him how he can tell me the time so accurately, he said, "It's easy. I remember that it was that same time yesterday, and I just know that this time has now reached that time." Is he putting me on?

*4/12/70*

I met an unusual person during my work shift last evening. Unannounced, he walked into the building with two young men, asking if they could visit with Jimmy Carruthers. Heard about this man since my first day at New Hope. Mike Edward is a professor at the university. He's a great guy. He's a son of a bitch. He's an outstanding professor. He's an opinionated bore. He's a truly unique man. He's a carbon of all the other do-gooders. He's a humanist. But he dislikes people. His photographic essay on institutional abuses was the first authentic step toward a reform movement now sweeping the country. He's a dirty bastard; his book was a rip-off that made him a bundle; his yapping is leading to the eventual destruction of New Hope and all the other state schools. He's a good and kind person. He's an evil louse.

*6/6/70*

Mike Edward visited the building this morning, again to see Jimmy Carruthers. After his last visit, I decided to read his photo essay *Hell's Capital*. Powerful stuff! Also read two of his more recent books, *Lives in Scale* and *Gehenna Falling*. He can write, often uneven and with parts that might embarrass some writers, but he's powerful and knows how to communicate. Had a short talk. As I suspected, Jimmy Carruthers is that same Jimmy first discussed in the photo essay and, later, in *Gehenna Falling*. Mike "found" him in Wallin Hall about six or seven years ago, locked in a toilet during the daytime hours and in a solitary cell from 4:00 P.M. to 6:30 A.M., a routine that hadn't varied for at least ten years. When Mike first saw him, Jimmy was 16 years old, not toilet-trained, unclothed, uncontrollable, a grotesque creature. It's all described in *Gehenna Falling*. Mike and one of his students, Bob Sumner, asked for permission to design a program to train Jimmy. Using an operant-conditioning approach, developed by Ogden Lindsley while he was still at Harvard and Metropolitan State Hospital, they were able to help him to such an extent that he is now, literally, a different person. As his mother said to me, "My son was dead. Now he's alive, a human being. He's clothed; that means I can take him out for walks or, even, off the grounds for a visit home. He doesn't soil anymore. He doesn't bite. He says a few words. He laughs. He's kissed me. He holds my hand in his. It's a miracle."

When I ask Dr. Edward about all of this, he appears uncomfortable, doesn't seem to want to discuss what he implies is too obvious for comment. When I press, he tells me that Jimmy's situation is no more a miracle than the case of Victor, the Wild Boy of Aveyron, Helen

Keller, Jody (another of Edward's subjects reported in *The Disfranchised*), and, possibly, thousands of others who have changed in remarkable ways. He tells me that these people merely are live demonstrations of the concept that capability is a function of practice and training; people can change—that is, can learn; intelligence is plastic; mental retardation—any retardation—is responsive to treatment, can be prevented in many cases, ameliorated in all cases, and reversed—cured!—in some cases.

Interesting man.

### 7/9/70

Met Mike Edward in the employees' cafeteria at noon. We had lunch together. Finally had the nerve to tell him that I write and to ask him what I've wanted to ask since I read his books. Been holding back, though. I don't want him to think I am one of those guys who suck around published writers to learn shortcuts to success or, worse, merely to be with writers so one wouldn't have to write himself. How can I put the question so he won't think I'm a phony or stupid? "Dr. Edward . . . Mike. Mike, do you feel any special responsibility to your readers?" "Only two; Hemingway said it, so did others, and I believe it. My words must be true; I must not lie. And, second, I must try to write as well as I can and about matters that really concern me. I must remain apart from such considerations as, for example, the chances that my work will be a commercial success, what's "hot" and what's passé, what's academically respectable and what isn't, what is difficult and what is easy. I must try to write as well as I can while I know that, to be honest, my work must also be flawed. I cannot only take the safe road. I write where my work takes me, rather than work where the writing is easy. To do that is to produce uneven books, parts of which still haunt me. But, that is both an excuse and a reality. I am not so naive—deluded—as to be unable to recognize this marvelous rationalization for my poor writing. Yet I'm not quite so delicate—or is it proud?—that I'll reject a very reasonable explanation for the unevenness of my works, and the widely different opinions of me. Yes, I also hear things and, for whatever reasons they have, what I don't hear is called eventually to my attention."

Very unusual man.

### 9/14/70

Had a cup of coffee with Mike this morning. We talked about writing stories. "Tell it well," he said. "Stories must be told simply and must involve people the writer knows, that is, knows in the sense that they ring true, are authentic and alive."

**9/16/70**

Met Cyrus Bernard yesterday. Mike Edward and he came to visit the building to see Jimmy Carruthers. I knew of Bernard during my student years in Boston; even heard him speak once at the B.U. Psychology Colloquium; he's a very famous professor at the school across the river. I've been told he's a close friend of Mike. Seems like an unpretentious nice-enough guy. Maybe I'll take a crack at his book on mental subnormality. People here say it's about the best available. I guess I should make some attempt to learn about this problem, not that anything theoretical will be of much help to me here or, at least, not as long as I'm a shit-shoveling attendant.

**9/22/70**

Just hang around Mike and you meet all the "biggies." Had lunch with Mike and Dr. Zelman Gabler today; yes, Gabler! I've been wanting to meet—to merely see—that man since my freshman year in Boston. Yet, today, we've had lunch together. I now understand a bit more clearly why a *New York Times* feature writer called him the synthesis of everything clear and everything opaque, with the analysis always pure and unique Gabler.

I understand his remark that, for some people, freedom is more important than life itself. But do I appreciate his immediate correction: "Freedom is always our most precious possession"?

**11/11/70**

Sat in on Mike's seminar yesterday, Gabler participating. A student: "What advice will you give us?" Gabler: "I don't give advice; I don't even seek it. But I think I don't give it differently from the way others don't give it. If you're honest with yourself, and work at what you must do, advice becomes irrelevant. You'll do what you must."

**12/7/70**

Had lunch with Mike this noon. We spoke about too many things, a couple worth noting. He told me that his brother Marv and he actually—no bull!—learned about the attack on Pearl Harbor after watching that now-famous New York Giants football game at the Polo

Grounds. Mike described the game—Mel Hein, Tuffy, Hank, the others I must look up someday—and the P.A. announcements ordering all military people to return to their bases, ships, offices, wherever. Strangest thing: not only did the game continue during and after the announcements, but actual notification of the attack was not made any time throughout the long afternoon; and, further, the people sitting near Mike and his brother appeared neither curious nor concerned about the unusual P.A. blarings; at least, that's the way Mike remembered it all. Funny, he spoke about that war as if it was real and people lost real arms and real lives. I think about it as I think about the French Revolution, knowing it happened but not believing it happened in my world. Funny, also, that those people at the Polo Grounds were unable to appreciate the momentousness of the event. Perspective is everything and witness hardly anything.

We also talked about writers and other artists who self-advertise. This past week, Mike had finally met Sophie Cott, a painter he greatly admired; in fact, he recently purchased one of her works—not only spending more than he wanted but also more than he had. The meeting was a disaster. Almost from the beginning, he disliked her—for her boasting, loudness, vanity and, most of all, her silly, embarrassing chatter about the "deep symbolism" of her paintings.

We concluded not only that works of art should stand on their own but also that knowledge about their creators does not enhance appreciation; such knowledge more likely anchors the work to the mundane rather than lifts it in illusion and magic. Most writers and painters are not as interesting as their works. But, that's as it should be. How many gifts should one person have?

### 12/18/70 *"Preoccupations with Myself"*

1. I want to write about my own life and be the hero of my own books. I want my work—which includes my fiction—to be of my experiences. My work and my life must be inseparable, and, therefore, my words must be a record of my past. All of my work, if not always diary in the narrow sense, must reflect only what I experience. It must reflect either what has happened to me or what I imagined might have happened to me. It must describe the action of the body, of the soul, or of the mind—but always only mine.

2. A person should not mistake:
    wit for profoundness
    callowness for courage
    thoughtfulness for caring;
    Nor should he confuse:

   prettiness with beauty
   loquaciousness with wisdom.
  Those have been my problems.

3. The writer might best look at history to comprehend his substance, but he should avoid the past as he seeks a rhythm for the work he is on. Style and timing should always be freshly created to solve the current need. Only hacks can get away with thoughtless formulas—and they don't succeed at other than hack work. One definition of the hack writer is he who can write without struggle because he's done it all before. The hack's words may be elegant, but the whole is always less good than the individual words or even major segments.

4. The surest way to please the reader is to give him something he recognizes or identifies with; most readers don't want to work at reading. However, that approach presents a problem if the writer has visions that his mission is to teach; for, maybe unfairly, learning requires one to struggle; "learning" and "changing" are synonymous. That which pleases the reader fails the teacher.

5. I am preoccupied with the process of artistic creation because I believe it is at the center for understanding all human development. Besides, it fascinates me.

6. Good writing must be judged good in spite of its flaws. But, good writing—poor writing, it really doesn't matter that much to the writer; what's important is that he writes.

### 12/19/70  "Preoccupations: Continued"

1. I am also increasingly preoccupied with a question that doesn't have any answer: although every one of us begins life smelling so good, looking so innocent, and encouraging such great hopes, why do we turn out the way we do? Something is terribly wrong with the development game. It's neither to be trusted nor—regardless of the process of artistic creation—understood.

2. Creating something, unfoldment, development, these are the things that matter, that require our attention, even as we learn that there are no answers that will be helpful. The puzzle remains; hence, the preoccupation.

3. A bright young fellow who volunteers here, Derrick TePaske, said something during coffee break yesterday that illuminates so many things. He's a photographer and, on a recent trip downstate, he rigged up a camera to the outside of his car so that it took one picture every ten minutes and another every ten seconds later. Each set of photographs—that is, those on the ten-minute schedule and those on the ten-minute ten-second interval—produced entirely different com-

posites. Then, one may ask, what is observation? Or do photos portray reality any more faithfully than, for example, poetry? Or can there be a *cinéma verité*? Or is hard truth true? Or is objectivity objective?

4. Had a cup of coffee with Mike and Sol Gordon, professor of human development at Syracuse, who is visiting the university for a lecture this evening. Dr. Gordon said something that I never thought about before: "Two problems confront the institutionalized retarded: They are bored and they become boring. A critical objective for their reintegration into the general culture is to help them to become less boring, more interesting, more appealing. Otherwise, they may well fail in the sink-or-swim of ordinary society." Mike said this is exactly the problem experienced by many elderly people. And the problem will intensify as we construct more and more special segregated places to place them—really a national network of concentration camps. He thinks we should rather take advantage of their experiences. For example, who doesn't enjoy stories of the "olden days"?

5. The more I dwell on it, the more I am persuaded that writing is less an exercise with visible language than it is an exercise in visible thinking—and, fundamentally, oral language is also the expression of one's thinking; all language unfolds from the basic element called thinking. This is why some people (I for one) don't write about their thoughts but write to be able to make their thinking known to them— not to others, to them. And, one of the problems with schools is that they deliberately, and singularly, train children to write only to communicate, never to think.

## 12/24/70

Christmas Eve. In spite of the trees, the decorations, and the carols, I'm not with the spirit. Seems as if the Department of Mental Health is ripping off Santa Claus. But, the day was not without some reward. Met a rather interesting guy, a resident named Adam Mack who was assigned for work in our building today. Works his ass off, is built like a middleweight, and is always laughing, telling jokes, keeping things loose. The other worker boys seem to look up to him. On the outside I'd never place him with the others here. Seems to be capable and mature. Maybe I've been here too long. Could it be, and so soon?

## 12/25/70 *Overheard at a Christmas party:*

"I thought you worked in a used car lot, not that you are a used harlot."
"Is there a difference?"

*1/2/71*

What a night we had on Thursday. I'll never forget it; not just because of the food and the wine; that was the least of it. Mike invited me to his New Year's Eve party. Me, drinking and arguing with Cy Bernard, Gabler, William Lee (a pediatrician causing some hell downstate), Morton Prescott (a physicist at the university), several of Mike's students, who I think are super, and lots others whose names I've forgotten. Had a great talk with Karl Viereck, Director of the University Psycho-Educational Clinic. Why do all of Mike's pals make the noises of anarchy? In his, oh-so-quiet, almost shy way, Viereck sounded more ferocious than even Gabler. In rejecting any conversation concerning academic freedom, he said—merely as an aside— that the matter isn't discussable. "To give the item time and thought is to make an issue of something that is not negotiable. We would fall into the trap of those who want to control us when we just agree to try to convince them of our position. We must neither beg nor demand. Unfortunately, we are among the very few remaining spirits who have even a semblance of freedom in this society that has evolved to control us—to control everyone, even the controllers! Not only is our freedom at issue, but we are among the last souls left to demonstrate that freedom exists. Without us, the concept may die and, then, everything would be dead."

I have a responsibility to keep an eye on that man. If he permits it, I may learn from him.

*3/12/71*

Heard it again, this time from Don Baldwin, one of Mike's students, attempting to explain to a classmate that their observational reports of our building had to be honest. That was more—much more!— important than the flow or rhythm of the words or, even, how "interesting" the report sounded. "All we can offer is the truth as we see and feel it." Glad I heard it just this way. I'll try not to forget.

*5/23/71*

Went to the university graduation this morning; Cy Bernard was awarded an L.H.D. and was commencement speaker. It was a time and place for advice, and even he complied: "Do what you are driven to do. Only worry when you mislead yourself and you stray from your passion. Don't be concerned by the uniqueness of your mission; that may be your strength during the long haul. Don't disdain or mock others as I hope you don't grovel before the gods of power or, even, beauty. Lastly, please excuse my presumptions during this talk. It's expected of me; take it for whatever small value it may provide."

**9/10/71**

After his long summer away, I saw Mike this morning. He came to the building to see Jimmy. He seemed upset; some guy downstate— the Superintendent of Brook Island State School—wrote a review of Mike's book, *Gehenna Falling*, and completely dismissed it. "I don't mind whether they appreciate it or think it's terrible. But not to be taken seriously by a man who I suspected was, at least, literate is a disappointment. I'm depressed."

You live and learn. Even Mike Edward gets depressed. There is yet hope for me.

**11/13/71**

Nothing like a football game with friends on a perfect fall day (learned in London this past summer that "fall" is an archaic Elizabethan term that is no longer used in England). And it's whipped cream on the cake when such a day is followed with a raucous dinner at the Edwards'. Ethel and their three boys always provide entertainment and things to think about later. We played a game after dinner: in one sentence, put down what you most want in life. I learned something about myself that evening. I said that I just want to write.

**1/1/72**

Another New Year. Another party at Mike's. Have to remember what Cy said: "Be a human being. At least try to do what's right. The rest will fall in place."

**3/3/72**

Bengt Nirje spent two days at the university. Received an enormous response from students and faculty. Must write about that visit someday.

**5/15/72**

Had lunch with Gabler. Good talk. He's angry. Another rejection from the National Institute of Mental Health. "So many people— academics!—are fearful, afraid to say what they believe, even what their 'science' has led them to believe. I will not be quiet; I will not join that mob of bureaucratic vermin, not even if it means I'll never be awarded a research grant. I will write and say what I think is the truth. *I* will decide what comes out of my mouth. Those vermin!"

*5/24/72*

Had dinner at Mike's last evening. He seems on edge, not happy. Hope the summer recess will perk him up. I need him.

*5/29/72*

Mike and I talked about writing through much of my third shift last night. Should think about the following points:

1. Writers, especially young ones, must be encouraged to write from their own experiences but must not be misled to believe that experiences are their only sources for material. Otherwise, what can they say after that first book about the family, the school, the love, or the war?

2. To write differently, the writer must think differently.

3. The writer must love writing more than literature. The love of the latter is easy and, therefore, is commonplace. To love to write is to have a passion and to seek a labor that is grueling. It's a gamble; and, even when the payoff is large, the labor is accompanied by an unreasonable price that the writer must always pay.

4. Don't take criticism too seriously, neither the positive nor the negative. Both types will be of little value to you, and if you buy one type you must contend with the other.

5. Writing, to be valid, must be honest, not cheap, unafraid, plain but with a style, a reflection of the writer's passions, alive. Humor, real humor, always helps but is always difficult.

*6/3/72*

Had lunch with Mike and Ethel yesterday. Semester is over; Mike's beginning the outline for a book, and he's reading existential philosophy, Bible commentaries, political science, sociology, economics, and theories of social organization. I don't know where he's going with all of this, but he seems to be on a specific task, and he's resolute about something—very resolute. He still appears troubled, but less so than he seemed several weeks ago, yet more preoccupied than ever. He seems to be thinking continuously about something and, uncharacteristically for him, he's adamant that others not intrude into those thoughts. It seems that he's not ready to share whatever is on his mind and—just a guess—the reluctance has less to do with us than with either the enormity, or importance, or fragility of that burden he's lugging around. On the other hand, all of the above might be the product of my developing imagination. Maybe he's just planning a new book (fact!) and this is how he's going about it (possibility). A parsimonious explanation; one point for Occam's razor.

*6/5/72*

Gabler and Mike visited the building this morning. They were deep in discussion, and I caught a piece of it before politeness and business matters cut it off.

EDWARD: "Why do you suppose that our country didn't evolve to another type of Hitler's Germany? Who can we thank for that?"

GABLER: "Hitler, himself! Obviously! I have no doubt that if not for the Third Reich, we would have inevitably become a truly racist mob of savages. World wide repugnancy of Hitler's gangsters saved us from ourselves, at least until now."

*6/6/72*

Who invented the concept of love? Or the name of something—anything—even things that ancient or modern folks make sacred? Who has proved that there is such a thing as a soul—or that "thing" is a thing? Where is it written, as proof, that we understand the things (things again!) that we label, or that they even exist? Is to name it to know it? That is, if we name it, can we grow it, or show it, or stow it? Not always! Sometimes the things we name can be loved, sought after, prized, hated, feared, consumed; but not touched, seen, or smelled. What is love, capability, brotherhood, asylum, mental health, mental retardation, the psyche, therapy, psychiatry, intelligence, education, power, wealth, language?

What are these things—yes, things as "thing"—that we shed tears and blood about? What is here at New Hope that is not invented, that exists independently of invention? What is New Hope?

> It happened that way
>   Fate, one might say
> A man comes in talking
>   We later go walking
> A stop for some Java; he calls it a cup

Uses strange slang, and his speech is abrupt
It happened by fate
And that makes it great
It had to occur
Here, mid the crud
Here, with those faces that circle the eyes
Here, mid the sounds encasing true lies
And here, where the people contaminate flies
Where the garbage is eaten and the dead
are in flight
Here I met Edward, and here I will write.

# Chapter 5

## A Day at New Hope

Michael S. Edward
College of Education and Applied Psychology
Center on Child Advocacy

Dear Commissioner Wiley:

On September 9, I had a nightmare. I awoke terrified, unable to forget the ghoulish textures and sounds of that experience. We were in the jungle, fighting—whom?

One of our men was hit very hard. His head was almost gone and parts of his body were torn away. He wouldn't die. He continued to talk, to ask for water, to hope he wasn't causing too much trouble. And my reaction? During the nightmare, or after I had returned to the real illusion—wakefulness—I kept saying, over and over again, "Die, die you louse!" The nightmare was not in his dying but in his living. I could tolerate death, but not life that does not resemble life, that is disguised as death but too obstinate to die. I was embittered with this man who was beginning to smell, with this offensive spoiled piece of humanity who had not the decency, character, and good judgment to die without the agonizing fuss he visited upon us.

Which parts of the above were in the nightmare and which were the aftermath meanderings of a disturbing experience is impossible to judge. However, as I drove that morning to the New Hope State School for a meeting with its superintendent, Dr. Lenz, I could not erase from my thoughts the inhuman wish I had for the death of another human being.

Say it is fate, coincidence, retribution, or immanent justice for moral transgressions of the night before. For whatever the reason, the nightmare continued at New Hope. That afternoon, I learned or reconfirmed several things I truly believe:

1. The realities of life can be as terrifying as our subconscious ghosts swirling through the blackness of those pits we construct in our brains between midnight and dawn.

2. Over a period of time, being forced to contend with "spoiled humanity" dehumanizes us.

3. We cannot tell people to act as human beings and expect that our advice or command will be heeded. Under certain conditions, people will behave as we suppose humans should behave; under other conditions, they will not.

On that afternoon at New Hope, I asked to see Goddard Hall—a place you have for severely retarded ambulatory male adults. Accompanied by the institutional steward and Joe Hanes and Dan Roberts of your central office, I revisited purgatory for the first time since our photo essay. Almost demanding that Joe and Dan enter that foul-smelling den of disaster—they preferring to go directly to lunch or anywhere else—we pushed ourselves into the rancid kitchen, entering from the sweet-smelling outdoors.

Stumbling amidst those buried lives, the indelicate care, the blatant and subtle pandemonium, were shapeless forms who milled about mumbling incoherently, incognitant, incognizant, inert. One hundred and forty-eight grinning, frowning, shrieking, silent, wasted, and forsaken brothers greeted us. Their welcome made me suck in my breath, made me clench my teeth—resolute in a purpose to expiate for some debt or abnormal obligation, to once again tremble through this bitter experience, see every room, every cell, every defiled body, and ask the same warped questions:

How many patients do you have?
How many attendants are on duty here?
Where are the solitary cells?
Why does it stink here?
God! How can you work here? *You* appear to be human.

We were taken first to the dormitory, where beds were lined—row upon row, sides and heads abutting—beds without pillows, without a sign that this one's yours or that one's mine, beds arranged and covered by the numbers assigned to men who long ago ceased to exist as men.

On several of these beds we saw huge mounds of tattered, colorless clothing, waiting to be sorted and stored. In the attendants' areas, closets, and even in one solitary-confinement cell, we noticed piles and piles of garments—unrecognizable, faded, and shapeless. As you know, Commissioner, these garments are assigned randomly to building residents and collected periodically on washday for eventual countless reassignments. I have read descriptions of the beauty and loftiness of communal life. Possibly, devotees of such systems have some valid argument. However, I am irrevocably persuaded that there is nothing implicitly uplifting or ennobling in communal underwear, and I feel certain that no political or welfare manifesto can convince me otherwise.

From the dormitory, we proceeded to the day room, that place in the residential facility intended to resemble most the family or living room. This is the area for group interaction and fellowship or, possibly, for television, quiet games, or parties. The Goddard day room is quite large, I should guess forty by fifty feet, contained by peeling walls and ceiling, and a cement floor—the center of which has a circular sewer of about one foot diameter.

Entering the day room, we observed fifty to sixty adults in varying degrees of nakedness—most of them completely bare, others with a shirt, underwear, a sock. Some were standing, others were lying on the cement floor, and a group was sitting or sprawling along benches that circled much of the room. In the center stood Mr. Anderson, the "matron," a young athletic-looking man. He was wielding a slop broom, seemingly trying to push the recently accumulated debris, feces, and urine into the floor sewer—conveniently installed for such purposes by our efficient engineering service. He was facing away from the entrance and, as the moans and other noises of the room were quite vigorous, we now accidentally became undetected observers.

I am not certain how many minutes we remained unnoticed. I do know that I walked to the left of the day room, having been told that an isolation room was located off that section. Further, I remember peering into that confinement window and observing a teenage boy wrapped in a blanket, lying on the bare floor of the cubicle—no bed, no toilet, just the hopeless, unremitting, and inevitable program toward the destruction of a man. I further remember that, as I turned to rejoin our group, I stumbled over one young man lying on the floor adjacent to the isolation room, and that that clumsiness, in turn, caused me to trip onto another one, lying nearby. Possibly, all of the aforementioned lasted no more than sixty or eighty seconds, for as I returned to the day room entrance, Mr. Anderson was still engaged in his sweeping chores. Why didn't I call out to him to announce our presence? I prefer to think—yes, I truly believe—our failure to make our visit known, to either shout out or stride out across the room, resulted from our hesitation to interrupt him while he was performing his work and our unwillingness to negotiate a walk through that horrible surrealistic, irrational arrangement of life. It may be that Joe Hanes and I huddled together, unwilling to retreat from the reassurance of our togetherness and the comfort of swift escape, if need be, through the exit an arm's length away. Of this I am certain: there was no mendacity to our behavior, if for no other reason than the fact (consciously obvious even to us) that we were overwhelmed by the situation and incapable of then planning anything so cunning as a secret observation.

We stared, gazing rigidly in fear and wonderment, for possibly a minute, no more. In an instant or two the setting changed totally. Mr. Anderson shouted some command at one of the denuded men who was seated on a bench. I did not hear his words, but it seemed that he was issuing some instructions or orders. Apparently unsatisfied with the man's reaction to his message, before our horror-struck eyes he lifted that filthy slop broom and, over and over and over again, beat it down upon the naked, cowering body, a steady stream of curses spewing from his enraged tongue.

As with all nightmares—at least those I have—this one lasted no more than two or three minutes. As with all nightmares, it is the preoccupation with the morbidity of our reactions that has lasting and telling effects on our personality and behavior. One may ponder why these fleeting seconds so profoundly disturb me, and, on the other hand, why those responsible for the system, and who perpetrated and were participant to the specific misdeed, toss off with incredulous disdain my indictment that evil inhumanity permeates that environment. I believe that any discomfort the superintendent and Mr. Anderson derived from the incident obtained not from the fact that a staff member acted cruelly but from the embarrassment and threat of my accusation, which was made forcefully and officially.

The question I ask is: What was so offensive to me but not to them? Rhetorical and essentially unresolvable questions usually expect no answer. However, I have an answer, albeit metaphysical and introspective. I cannot tolerate spoiled organic matter, especially spoiled humanity. I gag at the sight and smell of piled garbage and decay, with its swarming maggots and oozing slime that pulsates in its primitive living cellular and animal parasitic kingdom. Neither, I suspect, can you tolerate spoiled garbage, for did you not include in your newest building a specially built walk-in refrigerator for garbage—so it would not spoil between the time of its storage and removal to the institutional dump?

I cannot tolerate human garbage, and that is what these patients have been turned into, and that is how I believe they are now viewed at Goddard Hall.

It is always fruitless—more, a denial of rational life—to attempt to convince someone that supercrescence, filth, slime, all things scatological, and all things uretic are natural and, consequently, completely acceptable facets of our human eminence. Yet, there are those among us who, rather than conceive of and develop programs for people that are ideational counterparts to refrigeration and sanitary engineering, delude themselves and others into accepting and perpetrating environments nurturing human garbage. Their ministry is not education or social welfare. Their mission is not rehabilitation and a return to human dignity and participation. Their ministry is delusion and deception and hypocrisy—to accept for their brothers that which they would not tolerate in a barrel of garbage. They have traded their brothers' birthrights for a stainless steel walk-in cooler and have been able to accept and justify the coexistence of fresh unspoiled garbage and humanity turned sour and rotten. In so doing, they have traded their own birthrights and humanism. Words cannot describe how deeply all of this offends me.

Sincerely yours,

Michael S. Edward

# Chapter 6

## Autobiographical Notes:
## 1964-1968, and Today

I entered Boston University as a freshman in 1964. I was seventeen years old, with the burden of appearing much younger and—so I've been informed—seeming quite naive to others my age.

I matriculated in the School of Education and spent the freshman and sophomore years enrolled in courses dealing with general psychology, personality, learning, child development, the culture of schools, foundations of education, and a distribution of work in the sciences, mathematics, social sciences, and English. It was in Survey of American Literature where I met Miss Pennington. She was a graduate assistant, teaching the survey course and English Composition, and trying to complete a doctoral dissertation on the American expatriates in Paris between the wars. I was a second-semester freshman, and hers was the first academic experience that made me wish for longer days to read. The world came alive; Boston became a wonderful place to be. There were old houses, people to talk with, and more books than anywhere else.

That summer was spent at a children's camp, "counseling" a group of ten-year-old boys. Never before had I felt so good about myself. The kids and I really had something great together; actually I had been worried that I would bore them; relief! The summer also was the time when I began to write regularly. The nights were free, although there was the continual choice between illumination or privacy always to be made. Like moths on a summer night, where there was a bulb there was a crowd. Two things I learned about children's camps are that, in some places, electricity is a luxury, and, second, privacy—either the child's or adult's—is considered, at best, suspect and unwholesome. But I did find the light (usually the moon) and the privacy (usually a field), and I did discover that people—most people—could be damned interesting and good to be with. It was the very best of summers, even—especially—when the days became shorter and those mountain nights cold. During bad times I think of that summer, and I feel good just remembering things.

As before, fall registration was a pain, but I was given the courses I wanted, one being Pennington's Composition.

After class once, early in the semester, she nodded for me to see her. Would I come to her office—really, a hole with a desk, two chairs, and books. She wanted to give me a few things to read. Sure! Gee, she must think I'm pretty good, or pretty awful. She never—at least I hadn't heard about it—asked other students to come to her office.

"I'd like you to read these stories. They're good. Also, you might appreciate this magazine, *Poetry.*"

"Sure, thanks Miss Pennington. Don't worry, I'll return them soon. I wouldn't lose them. Gee, thanks."

"I'm not worried. Your stories are too complex and too simple, but you write well. You do not have the critic's cultivation, but you may have a bit of the artist's temperament; and, you do write well, almost poetically."

That's all. That was the entire discussion. What discussion? Just a remark, an answer, and—"You write well." I write well? I write well. I, I! Never, not if I live forever, will I forget what she said. And, she *knows.* She's an English professor; well, anyway, a doctoral student. She knows. At least, that's what I banked on; boy, had I banked on that tiny remark, that bit of marvelous news, that piece of built-in encouragement.

I read the stories, and wrote stories, essays, verse; and read—everything. And, for the spring semester, I registered for a course in eighteenth-century English literature, another in modern poetry, and a third with Pennington, English Composition II.

After our last meeting of the semester, Miss Pennington asked me what I was planning for the fall.

"I hadn't thought about it."

"Well, obviously, you will major in English literature. It's merely a formality for you to change majors and gain admittance to the College of Liberal Arts. You want to write, don't you?"

"I? Yes! Until you just said it, I hadn't thought about the future past the next book to read or paper to write. But, yes, I want to write."

"Then write. But, you must also read more—yes, more. Writing is thinking on paper. The important things that now interfere with your writing are, first, you're uneducated and second, you have so few experiences to draw upon."

So, for the next two years, I tried to remediate those of my more tractable educational deficiencies—which I'm still working on. Also, I started to come out from under that bushel. Now, one might say that, today, I'm free—experiencing all that life offers—yet surrounded by all of the collective crud and enslavement known to humans. What would Pennington say about all of this? Is this experiencing, living, or merely learning what dying is all about? Would Pennington say that dying, too, is part of life? If so, I'm a specialist, but—nevertheless— an expert, like most specialists. Is it my fault that my expertise concerning life is death? Things have a way of happening, and I happened into New Hope State School, as good a place as any, I thought, to read, and experience life, and write. At least there is illumination and privacy here.

Did I know that the place is hell's vestibule? And, if I did, would it have mattered? Are the only things that matter related to the light, and the time to write, and the books I buy and borrow, and the experiences, and this manuscript?

Will these be the days I dream of later? Will this have been the time of my life that becomes such time only long after it has gone and I can't deal with it? Will these be the places I want to remember?

Will I find the meld I've been searching for, the bridge from my love of words to a passion for something outside of myself? Will I discover a life here that will intrude into my writing, that will make my words live? Will I learn what Pennington had tried to teach, that the writer's words must become extensions of his life, not his life itself, alone?

Today, here, I may love words too much and life not enough. For its own sake, I should discover what living can better offer. And, where but here should I begin the search? Where but here might I learn that art can't be one's religion, although it remains his passion? Where else will I convince myself that, while art cannot replace human love, it may explain it—even more, expand it.

# Chapter 7

## Michael Steven Edward

I am a completely inexperienced biographer. Someday, I hope to be a writer, but in my realistic moments I have few pretensions. Today I can better claim that I am trying to *learn* to write. I am trying to get down on paper things that are honest, that ring true. But, if I must be labeled, I must be labeled an institutional attendant who tries to listen carefully. And Mike Edward is whom I have listened to most carefully.

This book is not biography; I do not have that skill. If anything, it is history—obtained from diary, memory, and fantasy—less analytical than observational, less scholarly work than ideational photography, less examination than reaction.

Chronologically, I met Mike Edward not long ago, but it seems now that there was never a time when we weren't friends. He was born in Brooklyn, New York, on April Fool's Day, 1927. At some time during his high school years, he learned that he was more capable than many of his teachers and much less capable than a few of his classmates. That understanding about himself generalized, hardening—with time, experience, and some formal research—into an unshakable, almost haunting, hypothesis that forms the core of his work and life, that has been the central question in every study he has undertaken during an unusually colorful academic career midway into its third decade.

Mike's abiding preoccupation—clinically, in teaching and research, even influencing his private life—has been in testing the hypothesis that intelligence is educable. That is, intelligence is a function of practice and training, as are all of mankind's capabilities.

During the years, his research and publications have dealt with several recurring themes, each inevitably relating to the hypothesis of human educability. The first such theme deals with the so-called nature-nurture question. And although there is little scientific evidence that permits definitive answers to this age-old issue, Edward concludes that there is enormous clinical evidence that man can change, that intelligence is educable. The work of Itard, the autobiography of Helen Keller, May Seagoe's biography of Paul, the research of Harold Skeels, Sam Kirk, and Seymour Sarason, and Mike's own experiences lend support to the educability hypothesis. However, evidence aside, for reasons dealing with the mission of teachers and others in the helping professions, Mike believes that this hypothesis is the only defensible hypothesis. For, as his collaborator Frank Garfunkel once said, "There is nothing essentially inherent in retardation to produce handicap. Further, it is not the mission of teachers and other practitioners to find out whether or not that belief is true, but to make it become true."

The philosophical underpinnings of Mike's activities are embedded in his belief that, as human beings, all people are equally valuable. Nirje enunciated this concept in his so-called "normalization theory." However, the ethical teachings of thousands of others since the beginnings of our civilization provide us with almost infinite expressions of this belief, and with some hope that we may one day take the idea more seriously than heretofore.

Yet Mike believes that human beings continue to have a penchant to segregate, to separate, to make pariahs of other human beings, and more than ever before we seem to be engrossed in such activities. He has examined study upon study that demonstrates this inclination people have to stigmatize others. And, though this is discouraging, certainly in conflict with normalization theories and humanistic concerns, there appears to be some notion today that people are beginning to discuss such issues, previously not considered proper or important enough for public examination. For example, possibly for the first time in our American experience, the myth of such terms as "mental retardation" appears to be partially understood. The so-called "efficacy" studies and nomenclature changes in "mental retardation," the black revolution, and other professional and social movements have led to a deeper appreciation that, for example, "mental retardation" is no more than an administrative term. It has little, if any, scientific integrity.

Mike's work has caused him to grapple with very complex issues; he is just beginning to understand that the world is opaque, mysterious, and secret, and the most important problems facing mankind are the ones that have been most effectively concealed from public observation and consideration. His work has also led him to better comprehend the necessity that some responsibility, some authority, some decision making, some priority setting be given—or be demanded by—consumers of services. Although it has been said in other contexts and about other matters, education and care are too important to be left entirely to professionals and their interests. It is not that professionals are less able or less trustworthy than consumers. They are different, with different agendas and priorities.

Recently, Mike Edward had described the mental health-mental retardation bureaucracy as a monolith. However, to understand what he meant by this, one must understand that the Monolith is not the institution or the segregated special class, but the absence of alternatives to segregated settings. The prepotent issue embedded in his political philosophy, not far from the surface of every argument he offers, concerns that single block of ideological stone, that massive, solid, uniform, no-option, no-alternative slot machine of one system— segregated and exclusionary placement. At the core of Mike's politics, polemics, and professing at the university is the argument that we must maximize variance in society and thus enrich everyone; second, we must maximize opportunities and options for all people and thus permit each person a truly equal opportunity to develop.

If one were to summarize Mike's work, the beginning would include a central statement concerning the hypothesis of educability. A second comment must be made noting Mike's observation that society has organized programs for "different" children and set priorities in ways to illustrate that people do not change, that alternatives to segregated settings are not necessary, that special classes and institutions serve us well, that intelligence is not educable—hence the discrepancy between Edward's major theme and society's dominating agenda. In a way, there is something Kafkaesque about Mike's work as there surely is about the Monolith, something of the men who would build castles to contain deities and who would serve society's institutions in so doing, while they build hovels for themselves; and, to out-Kafka Kafka, they create hovels within the shells of their magnificent castles. There is something Kafkaesque about departments of education and departments of mental health and other of our human creations designed to nurture people. Possibly Mike's work too is flawed, as we are flawed, because it is all a terribly complex matter and, in spite of his attempts and the attempts of others, even he has great difficulty seeing the hovels from the castles. He too is a victim of his own experiences.

I recently taped a brief radio interview between WNHC, our local station, and Mike, dealing with the Center on Child Advocacy, which he directs at the university. A bit of the typescript may reveal part of this man's history:

Q: Professor Edward, you have stated on several occasions that "building better institutions is not the answer for people with special needs." What is the answer?

A: We have never suffered from a lack of buildings, institutions, or good intentions. Further, there is no single answer to rectify the abuses of the past. But what have we learned?

First, institutions will never serve human beings in ways that satisfy our needs to be normalized, included, and involved.

Second, whatever the answers are, they begin with each individual, with me. Before I attempt to change the world, I must change.

Third, most of our problems relative to human abuse are *not* caused by cruel or particularly incompetent people. We have segregated classes, and all too many children with special needs are excluded from school because of conceptions of human potential that lead to the assignment of a segment of society to what I term the "human solid-waste disposal authority"—dead places.

Q: The Center on Child Advocacy is the only agency of its kind working toward the elimination of legally sanctioned institutional abuse. What is your definition of institutional abuse, and why study this problem?

A: Institutional abuse relates to the official mistreatment of human beings, either legally or otherwise, with such regularity and in such ways as to seriously impair the victims' views, and other peoples' views, of their humanity. Some people are victims of their immediate environment, others of their generation, the legally abused of both but more of the latter.

Studies of institutional and other segregated settings lead not only to the illumination of serious problems that are little understood in our culture but may, eventually, provide mankind with solutions to them.

Q: What stake do "normal" children have in the work of the center?

A: The center is concerned with human beings; not with defectives, or retards, or normals. Our mission is to remove the labels, the stigma, the separateness—those things that divide us.

Our work is as much for those you call "normal" as for those whom society calls "special." Our intent is to help the world become a normal place for all people—for my children and their children—for me.

Q: One last question: How have your work and the center's activities been accepted by your colleagues? A bit uneasily, I ask the embarrassing question concerning the attitude of your colleagues toward the center, in general, and you, specifically.

A: No need for any discomfort; I am not easily upset. I'll answer your question with a prediction. If I were to become ill and require hospitalization, I would not be surprised to see at my hospital bed a delegation from the state chapter of the American Association on Mental Deficiency. And I would not be surprised to hear the solemn words of Al Rosenfeld, our president, intone: "I am pleased to report that, by a vote of twenty-four to eleven, the Executive Board passed a resolution to wish you a speedy recovery."

Michael Steven Edward, married to Ethel Davis, father of three sons, Richard, David, and Lawrence, a graduate of Pennsylvania State University, Columbia University, and New York University, former special class teacher, now a professor of special education; at least in his mind, he considers himself to be a reasonable and, more or less, conservative man.

It was this man who encouraged a group of so-called morons, imbeciles, and idiots to revolt, to attempt to achieve what neither professionals nor parents, politicians nor executives, philanthropists nor influential citizens were able to understand, much less deal with.

# Chapter 8

## A Day in Wallin Hall

". . . and, as President of your Senate, I am informed by counsel that it is entirely appropriate to convene this extraordinary joint legislative session on the grounds of New Hope State School. Our great commonwealth, our governor, our dedicated superintendents and staffs, even we in the legislature, have been attacked and vilified, in spite of our efforts on behalf of the mentally retarded. Unfortunately, not all of the criticism is unjustified. We must do a great deal more for our mentally retarded. Hence, this special on-the-scene session.

"And, to begin our deliberations, it gives me great pleasure to introduce our keynote speaker, Professor Mike Edward, whose address, 'The Dark Side of the Mirror,' will be followed by our visit to Wallin Hall and other school dormitories and facilities. Professor Edward."

"In 1949 I started a teaching career and serious study with the mentally retarded. In the subsequent years, I learned some valuable lessons concerning this human condition. From the inspiration and clinical acumen of three great teachers and one institutional administrator, I began to understand and appreciate several major concepts concerning behavior, concepts that have been verified repeatedly during interactions with those generous children and families who permitted my intrusions into their lives. I learned some things, and I learned to believe some things:

"1. Man traditionally underestimates his potential for changing or, to use a more common term, for learning.

"2. Man's pessimism concerning the conditions of change becomes a self-fulfilling prophecy. We do not learn when we become convinced that we cannot or that we should not.

"3. Given proper conditions, it will be demonstrated that intelligence is a function of practice and training. That we have not been able to better stipulate those conditions is, I believe, less a defect of the general hypothesis than it is of our practices.

"4. I believe in a design of things. I believe there is something spiritual about. And, I believe the design for all of us holds nothing but good.

"But there is a dark side of every mirror, a side beyond inspection because it is without thought. And while the optimism and pride—the light—of our lives is for the gains made in civil rights, for our achievements in mental health, for the concept of the Declaration of Independence and the Constitution, surely a dark side in the evolution of our civilization in this mid-twentieth century must be reserved for the deeply unremitting, unrewarding lives of drudgery and pain we inflict upon our institutionalized brothers who are called severely mentally retarded.

"As some of you know, I once undertook a study of children and adults in state institutions for the mentally retarded. It was my purpose to describe in words and pictures the treatment of the retarded in these institutions, point out some of the more serious imperfections of their programs, and suggest ways to prevent or ameliorate problems. I expected that men of good will from all walks of life and all professions would then sit down at the planning table and seek viable solutions to the issues uncovered. It is not necessary here to discuss my findings, my recommendations, or the flood of encouraging mail and calls I received in response to that study. However, it may be instructive to mention that some of the reactions to the project were negative. I was subjected to mild direct hectoring and a good deal of indirect and secondhand pejorative assaults. I had undertaken the study of institutions and written the truth, as plainly and as simply as I saw it. As some of you may know, there is little reward in exposing the ugliness (or beauty) of certain truths. It can be a dangerous business.

"The view I am about to share with you today, in spite of its impressionism, its vagueness, its distorted textures and freely associated construction, is no less real to me than our photographic essay. This is the stuff of which nightmares are made and, if you will permit me, I will share mine with you. I have been to many state institutions for the mentally retarded, before and subsequent to the just-mentioned study. It is fitting that we concern ourselves today with one local state school. I accede to this reasonable decision. On the other hand, my remarks have a much more general applicability.

"I have been to the depths, believing all the time that I would awaken, as I always had before, from this most terrifying of all nightmares. And, as always, I did awaken—to the mawkish horror and degradation of Wallin Hall. I have walked beside its soiled waters where, floating gently by its day room shores, were the human flotsam and jetsam, the wasted and unfulfilled programs, hopes, and plans of countless generations of discouraged failures who were once known in this building as patients, attendants, and professional staff. I have filled my nostrils and inflated my lungs in Wallin Hall until every pore of my body felt the nauseating zing of seventy years of cankered rot that will continue to generate *ad infinitum* until the seams of Wallin's construction burst at the top and at the bottom and at its sides, until its cup of human refuse and despair runs over, until it drowns us all or causes us to realize, in time, what grief we perpetrate there. I have sat in Wallin's day room surrounded by desperately lonely patients. They were huddled together in body and spirit, defenseless against the elements, defenseless against assaults to their persons, to their souls, and to their consciousness. I have seen a hand reach out for mere human contact—if not for enobling friendship—only to see it pushed away by the fear and confusion of its intended recipient, as it was struck down by the fear and confusion of another recipient, as his was struck down, as his was struck down—*ad nauseam.*

"If these remarks today communicate any of my deepest thoughts and hopes, it should become very clear that I do not believe we can correct the blight of Wallin Hall and the plight of its residents with a new set of curtains, or a new paint job, or modern plumbing, or increased attendant staff there, or new words and slogans here. In the past, to one degree or another, all of these shibboleths and gestures were tested and found wanting. All were enveloped by the mire of that totally oppressive environment. We do not suffer so much the lack of structural architects and interior designers as we do the absence of ideational architects and moral interventionists.

"It is not that the amenities and courtesies are not appreciated. They are, for they demonstrate that, essentially, the conditions at Wallin Hall are *not* due to evil people. They are *not* due to any more incompetent or mendacious people than one finds in any large sociopolitical organization, such as your legislature or my university. Nor are these conditions due only to insufficient capital budgets and ludicrous per capita operating costs. Obviously, however, a more appropriate financial structure, a more tangible and pervasive method to encourage the considerable number of dedicated and enlightened individuals who are employed at the school, and better ways to cashier those who are incompetent, would reduce many of the problems you observe here and would make life habitable for those whose lives are now intolerable.

"But significant change, meaningful change, change all of us can be truly proud of, change that will result in objectively superior residential treatment—not subjectively relative improvement—cannot be attained until we alter our conceptions of human potential and our methodologies implementing those conceptions. In addition to a far greater share of the public treasury, in addition to more competent, more numerous, and more available staff, in addition to much smaller living and training units, we must develop more optimistic convictions concerning the abilities and potentials of those we call mentally retarded, however severe that retardation may be. As I have said earlier, the prophecy of incompetence and vegetation associated with the mentally retarded is self-fulfilling. Equally self-fulfilling can be the prophecy of competence and achievement.

"I have irrefutable evidence, from 24 years of clinical experience in the field of mental retardation, that *no resident* needs to live in a denuded state, needs to be a head banger, or needs to be locked in solitary confinement. I have irrefutable evidence that practically every resident can be taught to eat meals independently, can be taught to live among his fellows without being of danger to himself or others and without the use of physical restraints. I have irrefutable evidence that *all* building odors can be eliminated without the need for even more powerfully repugnant chemical treatments or electronic gadgetry that only masks the sources of these odors but does not eliminate the causes—filth and neglect. I have some substantive evidence that intelligence is educable, that is, people can change, can learn, and that this concept applies both to the retarded and those who minister to their needs. It applies to us too. We can change in our conception of human potential, and thus we can promote change in others. The lives of Anne Sullivan and Helen Keller speak volumes about this concept, as do the lives of Jean Itard and Victor, the Wild Boy of Aveyron.

"It is my hope that our governor, our legislature, and commissioners who have faith in these immodest claims will encourage us to develop a network of small community-centered programs, interrelated with a total community effort of preservice and in-service training and research. They would be in collaboration with our best universities where students in medicine, nursing, social work, education, and psychology may devote to our common need and common good their idealism, service, and professional skills. From such endeavors, we will develop new and vigorous ideas and ideals to better comprehend and confront that complex devastation, mental retardation. Without such approaches, we will continue to fund new curtains and paint jobs and, once or twice in a century, we will demolish old buildings. Without such approaches, we will continue to divert overwhelming problems with flimsy, thoughtless plans. We will continue to irrigate huge deserts with watering cans. Without such approaches, we will continue to create for every Wallin Hall we demolish, a new— equally large—residency which will be little more than the portrait of the original in infancy.

"This address need not be necessary to convince you of the imperative need—*at least*—to destroy forever the physical structures and the symbolic disease represented by Wallin Hall and other buildings at our state school. Some men dedicate their lives to building edifices. Before *we* can build, we must first dedicate ourselves to systematic annihilation. That these buildings continue to exist is either a massive indictment of our collective intelligence or a colossal testament to human inertia or incompetence. All that would be necessary to convince you that the danger point was reached many generations ago, that the point of no return—the time for physical and conceptual demolition—was passed before the oldest in this assembly was born, all that would be necessary would be to lead you now to these buildings.

"The triumph of evil requires only that good men do nothing. Good men, do something; do not turn away from this blight we call Wallin!

Do not rest until you can guarantee to all of our citizens that this building, and others, wherever they exist in our commonwealth, no longer serve the gods of pain, sorrow, and chronic hopelessness. And do not rest until, across the land, the hundreds of these buildings—and the philosophies they breed—are laid to their unholy eternal damnation.

"A little child we knew and loved was buried a few days ago, and my wife and I, in shocked awe, pondered the senselessness of a life taken almost before it was lived. However, Tim did live and, as all of us must, he died. Although his life was too brief, Tim lived a good life. We rejoiced for his life and now mourn his death. But the funerals for those in Wallin Hall come not with death but in life. For them, it is life that is the terrible avenger; it is life that we mourn. And as we are part of this grand design, we mourn for ourselves and for our helplessness.

"Believe that you are more than your brother's keeper. Believe that, while on this earth, you are his savior and he is yours."

# Chapter 9

## Psalms for Each Day

*9/27/72   Author's Diary*

## "Dreams"

Last night I had strange and continuous dreams. And each one brought me before the dead, to account for myself at New Hope. I was surrounded by people I knew—long gone uncles, aunts, old neighbors—and others I didn't know but who claimed to have once known me. They came from all places, from the highest and lowest of the heavens, from Gehenna, from the burning desert, the endless sea, the vale of misery, purgatory, and the capital of hell.

"Remember, to mislead another is a greater sin than personal evil."

"You are your brother's keeper."

"To curse or defame a fellow human is too great a responsibility for any ordinary man to accept."

"You are neither God nor immortal; all of your days on earth should prepare you to be worthy in His heavenly presence; they should not be to judge your brothers."

"Return to the Book. Do not change a single word—that would be blasphemous—but, in your head, think about each word; reconstruct your earthly values; test your understanding, and your charity, and your belief."

## (1)
## ON SUNDAYS

This is the first day of the week, on which the victims on earth used to recite:

A new week, a new hope for New Hope, let us rejoice for tomorrow and for our rebirth. Our eyes have seen all that is evil. Our ears have heard all that is terrible. Our bodies absorb the stinks of countless abominations. We know what no one else knows. And that knowledge causes us to be gentle.

## (2)
## ON MONDAYS

This is the second day of the week, on which the victims on earth used to recite:

We desire to reason with our captors, who are physicians who do not heal, teachers who do not teach, caretakers who do not care, reasonable men who do not reason. Therefore, we seek redress from God. If we must, we will bargain with Him. Let us go, and we will be Your living testament.

## (3)
## ON TUESDAYS

This is the third day of the week, on which the victims on earth used to recite:

Lord of Willowbrook, Lord of Letchworth, Lord of Belchertown, Lord of Pennhurst, Lord of Sunland, how long will you appear to judge unjustly and appear to show partiality toward the wicked? Save us from the hand of the state. Save us from those who walk in darkness and think it is light. Save us from those who are mean and think they are kind. Save us from those who destroy us as they claim to protect us. Save us from those mortals who would save us.

## (4)
## ON WEDNESDAYS

This is the fourth day of the week, on which the victims on earth used to recite:

God of retribution, appear! Some things are known to man, some but to God. Only You, God, know why those who crush Your people prosper, why those who slay the afflicted grow stronger, why those who enchain their brothers remain free. We are comforted, not in ignorance, but in knowledge of Your omnipotence and mercy.

## (5)
## ON THURSDAYS

This is the fifth day of the week, on which the victims on earth used to recite:
God is our strength. He teaches us that, although man is of few days, his life can be good; although he is full of trouble, his times can be sweet; although he is born alone and dies alone, his life need not be alone. For we, too, were strangers in the land of Canaan, and we know not to turn away from the lonely and despondent.

## (6)
## ON FRIDAYS

This is the sixth day of the week, on which the victims on earth used to recite:
The Lord is King. The Lord is our God. The Lord is One. He will save us. He will not forget. He will not let us forget. No mortal will ever forget what we have endured.
Remember.

## (7)
## ON SATURDAYS

This is the seventh day of the week, on which the victims on earth used to recite:
You have commanded us to rest on this day. So we will rest. But, our torment endures through the Sabbath for, today, we are not free and, tomorrow, there will be time found to make up our work You denied for the state. Our lives are everything that the Sabbath is not for; as the Sabbath is a glimpse of eternal heaven, we illustrate all that is hell. Therefore, we can rest on the Sabbath, but we have no Sabbath.

## (8)

This is the eighth day of the week on which the victims on earth used to recite:
There is no eighth day of the week, in the same manner that we are not on earth but elsewhere, as each of Dr. Skinner's Cumulative Records has its counterpart for us in Cumulative Degradation, as some light candles rather than curse the darkness while we extinguish them to avoid the visual horrors.

# Chapter 10

## Things Grandma Told Us About What She'd Heard, What She'd Discovered, and What She'd Created

#### (1)

An animal once asked a centipede how he manages to walk with all those legs. The centipede thought hard and long about the question and, finally, said, "I take the right front leg, then the. . . ." And, he thought more about the matter, and more, and he never walked again.

#### (2)

Not only violins but French horns must be included in the orchestra.

#### (3)

We forget almost everything we learn in school. All that remains is our education.

#### (4)

When the bellman is dead, the wind will toll the bell.

#### (5)

A distinction should be made between the simple and foolish person.

#### (6)

There is a difference between one who is innocent and one who walks in the path of the Lord. The former does not know right from wrong, has no knowledge of good and evil. The latter knows and chooses goodness.

(7)

Good and evil are easier to find than to understand, to label than to define.

(8)

Power and love, the two central concerns of human beings, cannot be taken, only given. Even the most humble and poorest person can deny these to the mightiest ruler.

(9)

Do not confuse popular ideas or folk wisdom with truth. Even distrust these things a grandmother tells the children she loves. Search for the truth always and know you are more right during the search than when you think you have found the truth.

(10)

Do not wait for something to happen. Do not wait for miracles or good luck. Do things now. Live for yourself and for those who are important to you. Live.

(11)

More people are punished for telling the truth than for lying. But do not convince yourself that truthfulness is foolishness.

(12)

One hopes to live a happy life. The trick—a rung up the ladder—is to work at what you would play at if you had no need to work, and to engage in affairs for which you already have enthusiasms.

(13)

It is more difficult to create joy than sorrow, to build than destroy. Avoid the easy road.

(14)

Simply, a community means people who are concerned with each other, if not always in intimate, always in genuine ways.

(15)

Most of us spend our lives trying to understand who we are. Yet, even when we learn something about ourselves, it hardly does any good, for most of us rarely appreciate what it is that we've learned.

(16)

To remember that there is really little worth remembering is worth remembering.

(17)

Things often go well among people with conflicting values, until some damn fool up and tells the truth.

58

(18)

The fire that melts the butter also forges the steel.

(19)

History harms those who ignore it or take it too seriously.

(20)

When things are going badly, forget the errors; when good, dredge them up. But, also, vice versa; any mix can help, as long as one tries to do something about his life.

(21)

Only humans travel through time. It is the essential trait, the problem, and the uniqueness of the human to remember what a life has been, what it might yet become, and that it will end. Only people can plan and change their futures before the end.

(22)

If there was but one army, would there be an army?

(23)

"It's better to give than to receive." Another way of saying that is "It's better to be the kicker than the kickee." Still another way is, "The only one on the field who doesn't get kicked is the kicker." Or, possibly, these three remarks are unrelated.

(24)

Society's current passion for dealing with the "aged problem" conjures up visions of earlier human managers who once-and-for-all time solved the problem of mental retardation. It's almost as if we are now witness to reenactments of other plans of earlier decades. Today we can observe modern efficient business types—corporate geriatric executives with a stake in American enterprise, some actually leading conglomerates listed on the big board. Yesterday, they were humanitarian physicians and psychiatrists creating those wonderful final solutions that became the cause of our lost innocence. And today we confront the same issues and, with seeming deliberateness, we commit exactly the same errors. Once the earth was scarred with state schools and hospitals. Today we plot to befoul our land with Sun City and the convalescent home, places where the sun never offers sufficient balm and where no one ever enters to be healed, but only to wait for death. And the insanity of it all is that we design these horrible places for ourselves—for us!—if we will but live long enough. There are no other enemies but those we call our brothers. And only we are theirs.

(25)

Although the early bird gets the worm, most of us forget that, had the worm been late, he would not have been gotten. For every point, there's a counterpoint; for every lucky early bird, there's an unlucky worm; for every person who is the victimizer, another is the victim. Think not only of the bird, but also remember the worm. For, who will deny, sometimes one thinks he is the bird yet, as it seems everyone else knows, he's but the endangered worm.

(26)

Science has but limited value in your business. Solutions to the problem of retardation do not exist because the problem is the problem. Otherwise, there is no problem. Your difficulty is with retardation, not with the people you call mentally retarded.

———————————————

# Chapter 11

## History and Prophecy

Why are all introductions like all other introductions? C'mon, man, get on with it. The folks here don't have all night, and I don't have all night. I'm getting angry; they came to hear me, not you. Smile, Edward, smile. They're looking at you. Just another minute more.

"As president of the New Hope Parents' Association, it is encouraging to see so many here for this first meeting of the season. I want to welcome the oldtimers back and give a special welcome to our friends. Further, I have been told that several teachers, attendants, and residents are here with us tonight. Welcome all, and now let us welcome our guest speaker who, I am certain, everyone here knows or knows of: Professor Michael Edward."

"I was asked to talk about those things that concern me most, things that have occupied my energies during the past twenty or more years. You will probably conclude from what I say that I am anti-institutions or anti-special classes. I am not.

"It may be true that I am not an advocate of either institutions or special classes, but the problem I have is not with institutions or with special classes; the problem is that there are no alternatives. With the rarest of exceptions, for certain people there are no alternatives to segregation in our culture.

"Mankind has a penchant to stigmatize its people. There are more of us segregated today than ever before. If one were forced to predict the future society in five, or ten, or twenty years, one would say that there will be more people segregated than ever before. And if one had to predict what the world of the institutionalized will be in ten,

or twenty, or fifty years, the prediction would have to be that institutionalized people will live lives similar to those lived by people in
today's institutions.

"In spite of new laws, new buildings, more money, things have not
changed very much since the sixties. Except in a very general way,
there has not been change insofar as humanizing the lives of the
so-called handicapped.

"Why? Maybe the most important thing philosophers teach us is
that the world is so secretive that it is nearly impossible to communicate the nature of man's real problems, that people do not know or
understand what the devil does, that they certainly do not understand
how to correct publicly sanctioned human abuse. How can I illustrate
some of these concerns?

"Not too long ago, we had a visitor to the university, Bengt Nirje,
who was once the Secretary General of the Swedish Association for
Retarded Children. He met with students and faculty on campus, talking about many things; about America, he said, 'You paid a price in
this country when you civilized a raw wilderness in just 100 or 150
years. You created a great civilization; you conquered so-called savages, built roads, bored through mountains; railroads came, great factories. You became the most powerful country on earth.'

" 'But,' he said, 'truly civilized nations cannot grow so freely. There
is still the frontier rawness in this country that surfaces in such places
as your institutions, and how you deal with your more grievous legal
offenders, and how you deal with your aged, and how you deal with
those children who do not do well in school.'

"In a later meeting, he told us what he had experienced just prior
to coming to the states. Bengt Nirje had taken a group of retarded and
blind adults on a skiing vacation. These were adults who lived in
state-sponsored group homes of one kind or another. At some appropriate time during the winter season, they decided they were going
to go on vacation.

"He described the marvelous week or two that these people had
in the Alps. There was something that did not sit right in my head,
however. I could not understand how blind people ski, expecting
that it must be infinitely more difficult than Bengt made it appear.

"However, it was really quite simple. What they did was send the
retarded folks down the hill. They kind of made a path, smoothed
down the snow. Then they attached little bells to the backs of the
skiers' sweaters. The retarded group went down the hill again, and
the blind vacationers followed.

"Now, just think about that! Think about an American state school
in this state or elsewhere. Think about sitting down with the often-

times incredibly dedicated, but always harried, superintendent of such a place and suggesting a skiing vacation; you would probably be committed! Planning a skiing vacation, or any other kind of vacation, is so far from the reality of the administrators' world that is not only incomprehensible for you or me to think in those terms—to do so may be considered some kind of mental aberration.

"Nirje left a little pamphlet with me which he had just put together. It resulted from a conference that a group of fifteen mentally retarded adults had in Malmö, Sweden. The purpose of the conference was to conceptualize their unmet needs.

"They gathered in small seminars. They discussed their needs. They discussed their wants. They discussed what they would demand. Then, their efforts were presented to the national government and the Swedish Parents' Association.

"I literally dare any professional or consumer to remember the last time a policy decision was made when the patients, or the residents, or the inmates, or the victims, or whatever they are called, had anything to say about what happened to them.

"I suggest that the problems of the so-called mentally retarded, insofar as being heard about their needs and demands, are very similar to the problems university students faced until a few years ago. The latter had very little to say concerning what goes on in their schools. They were almost considered by the faculty and administration as infringements of academic freedom. Then, groups of students had the idea: 'Hey! We are part of this! Maybe we don't own the university, but the professors don't own it either.'

"The retarded people who met in conference for a few days in Malmö put together a set of statements which, to me, has as much profundity as any I have seen prepared by professionals. The work of this group is but one of a cluster of examples to suggest that the disabled be part of the decision-making process, of program development, of priority setting, not just because it is the right and moral thing to do but because, in fact, the disabled have a lot to offer.

"Among a host of recommendations, these Swedish citizens found from their experiences that, as far as their leisure time is concerned, they want to be together in small groups. They want dance evenings with no more than 14 or 16 people. Under no circumstances do they want to walk in large crowds in town, and they do not want to ride around in a bus which says, 'Malmö Association for Retarded Adults'!

"Many other suggestions came out of the conference in Malmö. For example, the group said that each person should decide for himself what to do during a vacation. Despite complete or partial state support for these retarded folks, each felt entitled to a vacation, and one of his own choosing at that.

"Our problem in America is not connected with questions about vacations, or who decides when and where they will be taken. Our problem is getting some people out of the 1000 acres of the institution, some others out of the very buildings, still others out of their dormitories or seclusion rooms. There are people in our institutions who have not left their solitary cells in five or ten years.

"On the one hand, we are dealing with such painful facts as solitary seclusion, human experimentation, no alternatives to permanent segregation, and an America that cares little for some of its brothers.

"On the other hand, in Sweden, we encounter a group saying, 'We think visiting abroad is enlightening,' and by 'abroad' they mean another country, 'but we don't want to go with other disabled people; we want to go with the nondisabled, too.' I could continue with more examples, but I will not. I will not hurt you by sharing the injustices I have collected, because the list speaks volumes about discrepancies between Swedish culture and ours. Possibly, the most illuminating summary of the differences between our culture and some others was offered by yet another Scandinavian, who said that the people of the United States know more about the problem of mental retardation than any other nation. However, while we know more, we do less than most others. And, we do less in unnecessarily restricted environments.

"In fact, not only do we know more, but many of the great foreign programs for the mentally retarded, which we envy, were developed and tested and first reported in this country. The whole gamut of special education services, the design of programs for the so-called trainable, many of the great international medical, psychological, and educational achievements were created here.

"The Swedes, Danes, and Dutch came to the United States, visited our centers, examined our prototypes, read our reports, and they believed us. They returned home and implemented our experimental models, while we wrote our reports and then went on to other things. Business as usual! What else is new?

"Some have come to the conclusion that, insofar as people with special needs are concerned, the more things change, the more they remain the same. They say that, in spite of new laws and buildings and institutions, more Ph.Ds and more teachers trained than ever before, the world is very much the same. There has been some progress but, considering our good intentions, massive efforts, and immense financial and material investments, it has been negligible.

"We come back again—why? When one thinks about where we

have been during the last twenty-five or thirty years and where we are now, and where we are heading, one knows that the problem is in our heads and in our hearts. One knows that the problem has, literally, nothing to do with laws or buildings or appropriations of money, or how many people are trained in special education.

"The problem has to do with how a society conceptualizes what a human being is, with how a society begins to describe the criteria for being human.

"Since the beginning of my career, I have been engaged in but one work, sections of which have been published as research monographs, papers, prose, verse, books and, now, this talk. The focus of my work is man, his capability for changing, his perfectibility, his reform, mine. Possibly, this is my way of saying that, while living may be plotless, all lives are part of a Grand Design. Each man has value."

*9/29/72 to 9/30/72    Author's Diary*

# "If I Could Read His Mind"

Not bad, Mike Edward. A fair piece of rhetoric. But do you mean what you say? Would *you* take inmate demands seriously? For example, what if the residents of New Hope were to make demands, were to organize? Really to organize? Could they get away with it? Could they do something like that, really?

Read your prophets, Mike, and dream what you would dare to believe, what you know is complete bull, unthinkable. Read Ezekiel, Mike; he usually provokes enough to cause you to forget whatever persuaded you to read him in the first place. Dream, and forget the dream, as you fantasize, as you construct your own prophecies, Mr. Big Shot Ezekiel Edward:

> The Lord set Ezekiel in the midst of a valley,
>     a valley full of bones.
> And the Lord asked, "Son of man,
>     can these bones live?"
> And Ezekiel answered, "O Lord God,
>     Thou knowest."
> And ever since sons, and their sons,
>     prophecied over dry bones.
> For the Lord has caused men to reflect,
>     on His work and on His omnipotence.
> The Lord can cause breath to enter into you,
>     can cause life.

The Lord can enter the valley of the dry bones,
    can lay sinews, bring up flesh and skin.
The Lord knows if the bones can live,
    when the bones should live.
But man has been commanded to have faith,
    and to have desire that these bones will breathe.
The bones that are the whole house of Israel,
    the whole house of the mad,
    the whole house of the feebleminded,
    the whole house of all the abused,
    and all of the houses of all of the dehumanized,
All of these bones will live in their own
    green lands, when man believes they could
    and should rejoin mankind.

# Chapter 12

## How Long Shall We Cry?

When will you hear us amid the sounds of the day-room terror?

*10/1/72   Author's Diary*

## "Earlier Memories"

I was born on August 11, 1947, and because Mother was not addicted to astrology—that piece of science or religion was considered by the family as stupid, certainly, and profane, probably—there is no family record or remembrance of the specific time I entered the real world. But who cares? What difference does it make? We collect such a great deal of what we consider memorabilia, which are neither memorable, notable, nor worth the effort. We'd be so much better off forgetting such trivia as the time of day one was born—or even the day, I almost believe—and in remembering that which we pay psychiatrists and priests to help us to forget. We work at forgetting what's important to us and remembering what's trivial. Maybe that's all the human system usually tolerates, the trivia.

The average person has scrapbooks, slivers of long-destroyed goalposts, cheap trinkets, gold and diamonds that remain after we turn to dust. Even the average guy collects memorabilia to link his life to a history, to the total glory of civilization *and* the world beyond. He's a bit shy about it, circumspect too, not at all like a president of this country who actually believed that every word he uttered—*every word!*—must be recorded for the world's archives, for all of posterity, to the end of time. And wouldn't there be many of us to do just that too, given the opportunity and if it was expected of us?

The excesses we commit to become immortal, and all to no avail. A man lives and then he dies. The rest remains mystery.

Yet, I too collect memorabilia. I, with all the others, have things to remember. I remember the first time that I sat on a toilet; it is my very earliest recollection of comprehensible conversation with other people. I estimate that, at the time, I was no less than eighteen months nor more than two years of age. Sharp memory! Or heavy delusion.

The first time I truly believed that someone outside of the family had genuine respect for my capabilities was in the tenth grade. Mr. Shukoff, a tiny and very old teacher of algebra, was on lunchroom duty at James Madison High School. As young people of that age often do, the group (which to this day remains as the closest of friends and enemies) indulged in much bantering, arguing, one-upmanship, and boasting. Old Shukoff listened in; it may have been interesting, or it may have recalled things to him. Possibly because we would have discussed algebra anyway, possibly because Mr. S. seemed interested —therefore, who could resist involving that comfortable and respected gnome?—whatever reason, we invited Shukoff's participation in ranking each of us in mathematics. Seymour had the highest grades, undoubtedly a brilliant student; Salvatore—Snookie—likewise, was an A student, destined for Harvard (where he eventually matriculated); but I understood mathematics. I ranked first because I knew how to think. That was a scene I will never forget. It has been my inspiration for all the years after that day, and Shukoff became my prophet. How we contrive to fool ourselves to remain ourselves. How one turns to memorabilia and prophets for sustenance long after the trinkets and supporters have lost their shine or faded away.

New Hope has given me many things to remember—some that will nurture my mind and soul, some that were horrible and will be remembered because I learned—changed—as a result of the experiences. Will I forget the day I spent reading the court transcripts of the Nuremberg [or Nürnberg] trials and finding that these orderly demons required doctors' prescriptions—genuine Rx's—for each murder; will I ever forget that time—I was thunderstruck!—when I realized that, here at New Hope, a doctor's prescription is required to shock, to confine in solitary, or restrain an inmate?

So I record and grope for understanding and put away things to remember for the long days and other things to remember when I'd rather forget. Each of us saves for a lifetime, as if that's all a life is for. And who can say we are wrong? Who will not agree that one's lifetime is, other than his memories and fragile hopes, what he leaves to his fellows? Or what we take from him?

*10/3/72   Author's Diary*

## "Observations and Reactions: August-September"

Who will predict how that which follows will be remembered or forgotten, will be thought about or submerged? What have I learned from these experiences and what might I teach?

There are points and counterpoints, not adding to the complexity of institutionalism, but being the very substance that is the institution. The legislature allocates an additional 10 million dollars for this fiscal year; now, finally, institutions can be cleaned up. Now, finally, inmates will receive decent care; that is, the 10 million dollars will permit oranges now and then for inmates' breakfasts.

There are choices to be made by the inmates. "When do you want to go to bed, eight o'clock, nine o'clock, or ten o'clock? Did you say nine o'clock? Sorry, you can't go to bed at nine o'clock."

Who makes decisions in institutions? Administrators, professional staff, attendants? Do the inmates? And, if they can't, who can? Who is competent? Who is incompetent? Is there something finite called "competence?" If there is, what is it? If there isn't, then what are we talking about?

"Move, you dirty stupid son of a bitch. Move, or I'll kick you again. You disgust me. All of you disgust me. You're all animals. I can't look at you, stinking, slobbering animals. Pigs! Animals! Crud! Slime!

"Shut up. Stop crying; I didn't hurt you that much. Oh, shut up. C'mere, I'll give you a cookie. That will shut you up."

I have climbed mountains but missed reaching lovely heights. I have scaled precarious peaks while stumbling on familiar ground. Man has accomplished much, but what has he accomplished? We have done our jobs. But what have we done? Does it matter how high one climbs, how hard one works, how much one completes, how difficult the task? For where does a man climb? Why does he work? What are his ends? To what end are his means? He who engages himself for the devil finds something worthy in his slothfulness and would accomplish proper deeds by his laziness; his industry further faults him, while the good man can contribute only good. He who believes that mountains are themselves important, and scaling them is itself an accomplishment, may know not the difference between an object and its relevance, nor the virtue in thought, nor the dependence of man on his ideals.

Drugs, sheets, camisoles, seclusion, control, control, force, tie him, hit him, scare him, separate him, how else to control this mob of shrieking, howling, dirty, naked animals? What will the state, the department, what will *you* give me to do the job better? What? Two more items? A few more dollars? What, you bastards?

      Mutism, nudity, and fetters are the enemies
         of the civilized.
    And language, clothing, and freedom are the benchmarks
        of civilization.
    Language prompts a man to engage symbolically
        with other men.
    Language prompts him to communicate what
        he cannot demonstrate,
    To demonstrate what he must communicate.
      Clothing permits a man to walk among other men.
    Permits him to speak out
        the larger society.
    To physically and spiritually go beyond
        his room and his pallet.
    Freedom persuades a man
        that he is a man.
    Persuades him that
        there is dignity on earth,
    That civilization
        is for all men.
    What are the benchmarks of civilization?
    What but noise, and talk, and laughter,
    And crying, and sighing, and responding,
    Giving answers, asking questions, prompting,
    And seeking out to touch, to hold, to caress.
    A cover, a dress, a robe,
    A cover to hide the flesh and free the body,
    A cover to soothe the wounds,
    To conceal the trembling uncertainty,
    And man's unshakable humility and unquenchable vanity.
    And freedom!
    Freedom to walk, to talk, to think,
    Freedom to contemplate one's destiny,
    And contrive one's future,

To leave, to stay,
To wait, to flee,
Freedom to disdain that which another man loves dearly,
And freedom to cherish that which all other men disdain.
Mankind, if you still can,
Return the incarcerated to civilization.

"Hey Schmidty, want you to meet Mike Edward, Professor Mike Edward."

"Good morning Mr. Smith. New here?"

"Yes, just started about two weeks ago. Name isn't Smith, it's Schmidt. Lotta Smittys around, but I guess I'm the only Schmidty. Just call me Schmidty. Forget the Mister."

"Fine, and that goes for me too. You have quite a job here in Wallin, Schmidty. I don't know how Carl can do it, year after year, and he seems to enjoy it. How do you take it Carl?"

"It ain't bad, Mike. Was better when we had more worker boys, and before you do-gooders started nosing around here. Mike, you know I like you. We've been kinda friends for a long time. But, what'd it get you—with that book of pictures about New Hope, except a lot of good people sore at you? Hey, you don't know how many of my friends ain't your friends no more. We've been into a few things together, Mike. I thought you were one of us, even though you're a professor. But how the hell can I trust you? Every time I see you now, I'm looking for the secret camera."

"You'll never forgive me for that photo essay, will you, Carl?"

---

The creature cries first, as the soul cries
    most persistently.
The needs of the flesh precede the yearnings
    of the heart.
When man's belly is satisfied, devotion
    turns to the mind and the heart.
What man lusts for, initially, are not what he
    hungers for endlessly.
What man hungers for, each man must find in
    his own manner, and in his own time.
And, what each man finds does not satisfy the
    hungers, but deepens the pit.
What is it that lies at the bottom of the pit,
    at the endless and formless need?
Is it the triumphant and noble man,
    the vain and glorious seeker and taker?

*Is it what man seems to appear as,*
  *or is it what man seems to avoid?*
*What manner of man stands there?*
*What manner of man is the Essential Man?*

*No man knows, yet each man must ponder*
  *that question.*
*No man dare know, yet all men dare not turn*
  *aside from such thoughts.*
*And, as each man seeks his answer,*
  *each man must offer his personal truths.*

*The truth that each man finds a relationship,*
  *as he seeks a oneness and uniqueness with self?*
*The truth that man is not an island,*
  *nor is he the sum of a maze of bridges?*
*The truth that man is not dust to return to dust,*
  *nor was he, nor is he, eternal?*
*The truth that each man envisions his truth,*
  *as he strives to deny the truths of others?*

*Man hungers to change,*
  *to plan for his future while he anchors his present.*
*Man hungers to grow,*
  *while he denies his need to change.*
*Man hungers to improve,*
  *while he behaves as if his reasoning is omnipotent.*
*Man hungers to be,*
  *to struggle, to find, to sense.*
*Man hungers to act,*
  *on his terms, or on the terms imposed upon him.*
*Man hungers to feel,*
  *with others and alone.*
*Man hungers to be alive.*

---

"Hi, Mr. Johnson, Mr. Schmidt."

"Adam, say hello to Professor Edward. Mike, Adam is one of our new worker boys. He's a good boy, too."

"Hello Adam. Good to meet you."

"Hello, Professor Edward. I heard you talk here last week, uhm, Tuesday, when the politicians had that big meeting, and Sunday, with the parents. You said some good things. I really liked it."

"Did you, Adam? What do you think about institutions? What about New Hope?"

"Well, I don't know very much about these things. I. . . ."

"You don't? You live in an institution. You should know a great deal."

"Well, I like this place. But I think you're right; I don't think we should be mean to the folks here. I saw your picture book awhile back. One of the attendants showed it to me. Said you were O.K., trying to make things better for the patients. But I like it here; even though, sometimes, I feel bad for some of the guys. Sometimes, I feel bad for myself. Not because anyone ever treated me mean. But I get a little lonely. It's like I'm the only one alone in the world, and everyone else is together. Know what I mean? But I like it here, like it a lot."

# Chapter 13

## Views From Monoliths
## Behind Windows to Nothing

"Adam, we meet again! Are you staying for the meeting?"

"If it's O.K., Professor. I heard you were gonna talk to some special conference. Mr. Johnson said it was O.K. to come just so long as I finished my work. And Pop, back in the dorm, knows I'm not a troublemaker. During my off-time I can do what I want. That is, if it's O.K. with you?"

"Sure, Adam. I'd like that fine. Let's talk sometime. Maybe I can learn a few things from you about institutions."

"Huh? Oh, sure. That'd be nice."

"Ladies and gentlemen, we are grateful to New Hope for the use of their facilities tonight. And we are grateful to all of you who agreed to participate in this first formal meeting of the Policy and Action Conference. As we promised, the business meeting was short. And, as we also promised, this next part will be even shorter. Professor Michael Edward has agreed to address this group, to keynote a discussion leading to the initial setting of conference goals and plans for action. With your help, we will break the Monolith. And, to accomplish that, the first step is to develop a set of goals and principles that each of us must examine and, hopefully, endorse; a person has values and priorities that he should seek to have recorded for public examination. And now, it gives me pleasure to present to you Mike Edward."

"Thank you, John. The Policy and Action Conference is a union of consumers, parents, professionals, attendants, students, their professors, great and ordinary—each concerned with monoliths, with departments of mental health, with the inner city, with public schools, with the legislature. I speak on behalf of all who have asked or wondered what our people have become. We are a union of the once-powerless who remember the joys of unhurried and comforting walks on a summer day; we seek the right to such feelings for all people, for the still-lucky ones, for those who may have once enjoyed them, and for those who have always been denied simple and essential freedoms. Especially for the latter, we have joined together on behalf of all inmates, on behalf of all ghetto children, and—to a degree—on behalf of each of us living through these difficult times.

"We seek a society where leaders will not merely lead but will be led by greater visions and authorities than they possess—and a society where the people will be led because they are independent, because each person is truly free. We envision a society that will be free of dehumanizing and debilitating state-sponsored domiciles, a society that will evacuate human beings from any facility that abuses or enslaves. We want to create a society that has compassion for all those who are saddened, yet comprehends the differences between the man who regrets his own lost years and the one who worries for his brothers. We think about a person who not only is sad for those whom the world causes to suffer but who also weeps for his own zealousness and for himself. And, possibly today, each of us is that person.

"We have created a conference that earlier reformers, were they here today, would join. We try to unite, not around specific task orientations but around powerful ideologies, not around special means but around a consensus of humanistic ends, not around silly slogans thoughtlessly chanted but around the infinite perspectives of a complex dilemma. We try to describe and understand the subtle as well as the flagrant, ennui as well as flailing arms and diffuse excrement, and pandemonium as an extension of the best-managed 'model' institution. We try to act as if Itard and Howe, Dorothea Dix, Helen Keller, and Emil Kraepelin are our judges. We must attempt to convince others—and ourselves—that the state does not own a man, that the state controls but may not buy or sell a human being, that I may destroy myself, but the state has no right to my self or my corpse, nor to my feelings or mind or spirit. We try to illuminate the irony of the state that is permitted, by law, to take or reduce my life, while I—who should be the owner—may not, under penalty of fine or imprisonment, take my own life or cause myself bodily or moral harm. The state may, with provocation, kill me, institutionalize me, seclude me, drug me. But I, who should own myself, may not kill myself, scandalize myself, or dehumanize myself. What the state must be restrained from executing should become my inalienable prerogative. The state—as it substitutes pills for straitjackets and therepeutic isolation for solitary cells—does not change in the truly important dimensions. For it demands that each of us bend and twist as we scrape low to say grace and pay homage to it. Long live the state and to hell with man—even, exquisite irony, to hell with each man who represents the state. Man once manufactured the state and, now, the state manufactures man. The state is now the apotheosis of man! Possibly, Hemingway thought of the state when he remarked, 'All things truly wicked start from innocence.'

"Collectively, and each in his own way, we engage the Monoliths that special education and mental hygiene have become in our time. Yet, we are not misled about those with whom we must do battle. The Monolith is not merely the special class, not even such a place as the Brook Island State School. The Monolith—the traditional special education and the traditional mental hygiene system—is the total environment planned and implemented by the city, the state, the institution, the school. And, the problem often is not with good intentions but with a limited vision of human potential and what the world may yet become.

"Are there not some informed men who share these concerns? Surely, there have been many—though not nearly enough—who tried to reshape our styles of living and thinking. There have been some among us who understood the difference between feeding and eating, and between eating and dining. But all their concerns seem to have led to meager accomplishment, to trivial common good! And so our concern, and this hopeful conference, yet with small hope. For, in spite of some claims that it is darkest before dawn, one may yet encounter terror at high noon. And one may thus conclude that man's days can be as black as his nights."

# Chapter 14

## Cyrus Bernard

At age thirty, Cyrus Bernard may have been the most influential psychologist in the field of mental retardation. His book, *The Correlates of Mental Subnormality,* was an immediate success, and the current fourth edition remains a classic text. Nevertheless, at age fifty, Cy Bernard appears to be less the dominant figure than heretofore. Skinner, Lindsley, Zigler, Kirk, Dunn, Cruickshank, Heber, Birch, and Kephart are names that some believe are more prominently associated with the field. However, with the exception of Skinner, Bruner, possibly Maslow, possibly another, no one has published more regularly in psychology. And further, none of those great psychologists has had the profound and pervasive influence in the field of mental retardation that can be claimed for Cy Bernard. However, even more important than his scholarship, to work and study with Cy Bernard is a singular and life-catching experience. For, Cy has students, but each is his colleague; and, as often as not, his colleagues *qua* colleagues are also his students. Simply stated, Cy Bernard is not only a great scholar but also a great thinker. He is not only a great conceptualizer but also a great communicator. He not only teaches brilliantly but his students also become profound learners. He demands a great deal, but mostly of himself. There is freedom with him because he is so free. He is the living embodiment, the demonstration that only as free and independent people will we learn and grow.

It is Wednesday, 8:50 A.M.; the plane from Boston has just taxied to the airline terminal. While Mike is waiting for Cy, he thinks about New Hope and the glimmer of an impossible idea.

"How was the trip?"

"Fine. What's on the agenda today besides the Psycho-Educational Clinic?"

"I thought we could spend the afternoon talking, maybe take a walk on campus. It's a nice day, and I have things on my mind."

'Let's start now. Fill me in. You look troubled."

"Cy, how do you conceptualize power?"

"It's too early for riddles. You're bursting to talk. What's on your mind?"

"What we've done together all these years! The development of the clinic, the early education study, all the planning to change institutions; yet, where are we? Is the world different? Are teachers better trained, that is, not just better but in some relevant way? Are the institutions different?"

"Get to it, Mike. There's about fifteen minutes before we go down in the pits, between here and the campus, and, you know, once the clinic begins, and we see the children, and we meet in seminar, and the questions begin, there will not be time."

"O.K. It finally appears possible! I've got the notion—not really me, there are lots of reasons and lots of people involved, including you—the notion that, in the last analysis, each person is responsible for his future. Further, in the last analysis, each person must do something, something deliberate, to ensure the future he wants."

"Who can disagree with that? But you're being very theoretical, very academic. Get to the point."

"Quite to the point, is it unreasonable to conclude that even inmates of state schools and hospitals must assume responsibility for their futures—or the consequences may not be in their best interests? Is it unreasonable to speculate about the possibility that people, though judged incompetent by the state, may be competent to stipulate what their futures should be and to work to achieve those futures for themselves?"

"I don't think it's unreasonable to expect that so-called mental patients can take responsibilities for their futures. In fact, I think it's not only reasonable but it should be part of American law, as it is part of English law, for the inmates at New Hope to have the freedom to leave whenever they wish. You know that even in your goddamn state there are efforts now to recodify the commitment laws. I think that, pretty soon, residents of state schools and state hospitals will have those options. But there are ideas in your head; Mike, that go far beyond voluntary hospitalization. Explicitly, what is the bottom line of your thinking?"

"I think the time is right to help organize a revolt of these inmates, a revolt that will close down New Hope forever and lead to what everybody has been unable to achieve—guaranteed humane treatment and freedom for every inmate whose human rights are now being violated. I am thinking about the possibilities for organizing a successful revolt at New Hope."

"Christ Almighty! We had better begin that walk as early as possible. We need to do a lot of walking and talking. If it is any comfort to you, I don't think you're crazy; at least, I haven't yet arrived at that conclusion—although you tempt me. Christ! Your moral judgment argues against your better judgment. God help us."

# Chapter 15

## A Walk on Campus

"Good session, don't you think?"

"As usual. But, let's talk about New Hope."

"Cy, I've said it all. I'm thinking about a revolt."

"How? When? Who?"

"Curious, that you didn't have to ask *why*. Most of us know why. Only an insensitive or ignorant person would ask why. Your questions are comforting. It's obvious that revolt is, if not the only way, an understandable—not crazy—way."

"O.K., for argument's sake, agreed. But, how? How do you plan a revolt of incompetents? That's the essential question."

"Are you sure the inmates are all incompetents?"

"All, no, certainly not! But what about the obvious incompetents? The bed patients? Those who can't make decisions? Do we have obligations not to involve them?"

"They are involved. Lying in bed uncared for is involvement. Sitting, unattended, on a day-room floor makes them more involved than you or I. Not receiving physical therapy, causing a man with spasticity to become more spastic, involves him. It isn't that your so-called incompetents aren't involved. Rather, they are involved, 100 percent, and have no way of participating in the 'how,' the 'when,' the 'who,' and —in this regard—the 'why' of their involvement."

"Some people might say that you would be using these unfortunate people for your own ideological or political ends."

"Those people would be partly right! However, aren't the inmates being used now for other ideological or political ends?"

"O.K. This is all sophistry. Again, the question remains: How do you convince or commit nonverbal and nonreactive people to a cause that they can neither comprehend nor respond to?"

"Obviously, this is the logistic problem. Strategically, however, we are talking as if we agree that the revolt is appropriate."

"Mike, I don't know how to tell you this, but you have just made a leap from premise, to premise, to premise, to action that is not founded on either evidence or agreement. All I have admitted, so far, is that the concept of revolt is less an issue, less a bizarre issue, than how one would achieve revolt. Please don't think that I have concluded that revolt is the only avenue that can now be taken."

"Fine, Professor, let's review other possibilities," said Mike, ironically.

"I don't have an answer to that one. On the other hand, when Hercules cleaned out the Aegean stables, he wasn't required to replace all the crap. Because I can't give you a satisfactory alternative to revolt, that is not reason to agree that revolt is a viable solution to deinstitutionalizing inmates in the United States."

"Then what is your major concern?"

"The inmates! You're using them. Some could even die in a revolt."

"Some are going to die today, and tomorrow, and next week, right here, because of the treatment, or the nontreatment, or the neglect, or just the way things are here."

"But do you have a right to subject these people to other dangers, new ones, where the payoff may be very meager if not negative and destructive?"

"Knowing what we know, do we have a right not to?"

"That's the question."

"Look here, Cy, look at this beautiful mosaic on the wall of Crouse Hall. What Ben Shahn did here, in a way, communicates what I'm trying to say now. We've seen this mural 50 times, maybe 100; yet, each time we talk as if we admire only the art. However, I admire the words of Sacco and Vanzetti even more. Look at it; see what is says:

> If it had not been for these thing, i might have live out my life talking at street corners to scorning men. i might have die. Unmarked, unknown a failure. Now we are not a failure. This is our career and our triumph. Never in our full life could we hope to do such work for tolerance for justice, for man's understanding of man as now we do by accident.
>
> Our words our lives—our pains nothing! The taking of our lives—lives of a good shoemaker & a poor fish peddler—all! That last moment belongs to us—that agony is our triumph.

"What does somebody live for, Cy? What does his life mean? People should live for a purpose, as others die for a purpose. Gabler said it too; freedom may be more valuable to a person than his life."

"But be careful. Don't sacrifice other people. Sacrifice yourself. There is an old proverb that tells us that when somebody knocks on your door to ask you to sacrifice yourself or something you value for a good cause, bolt the door and pull down the shades."

"Don't think I haven't thought about that. On the other hand, is there another way? It isn't as if people aren't dying now. It isn't as if people won't die next year, or next century, unless something is done to destroy these institutions. It isn't as if we have a choice, that there can be legitimate reform, that change can take place without the possibility of people dying. Is it enough to say that I will participate in the revolt? If I join with these inmates, if others do—students, you —aren't we, too, risking our well-being and our futures, as we ask these inmates to risk theirs? Does that make a difference?"

"Maybe it does. What are the chances?"

"I don't know. But I think they are better than whatever chances we have otherwise."

"O.K. Let's agree that revolt is both sensible and morally defensible. How many people do we have who will participate actively, who can make decisions, who can control or comfort and encourage those unable to make decisions?"

"Of the 2300 inmates, I estimate that at least 2000 can participate to some degree. There was a study done in New York recently that the State Department of Mental Hygiene sponsored. They—*they!*—estimated that about one-third of the residents of all state schools could leave tomorrow, and another third could leave with only minimal additional supports in the community. I estimate that, of the remaining one-third, very few would be so incapable as to require full-time and total supervision."

"How many of these 2000 could we reach, and how many would agree to work with us during the planning stages? How many could be trusted to work quietly? How many of the inmates are capable enough to take leadership in this revolt? And, how many would?"

"I don't know. But we could find out, slowly, and carefully, one by one. There is a young man, Adam Mack. Maybe you've met him. I think he might be interested. He's what they call a 'worker boy.' Possibly, you've seen him during one of your visits to New Hope. In any event, he is quite capable, articulate, and, I think, he is a leader among the inmates here. There are inmates whom you and I know. And there are inmates whom others know. It will take time. However, I think we could recruit 50 or 75, possibly 100, inmates to work with us."

"Mike, if we could recruit 100, capable of dealing with these issues and taking leadership, maybe there would be a chance."

"Sure. Besides, Cy, there are a number of others—not inmates—who would be interested, who would join us. We have students who have examined these issues and visited many institutions. There are professors, not only in education and psychology—elsewhere in the university. They too have been very concerned about life in these institutions. There are community people, ordinary citizens, doctors, lawyers, possibly some of the local farmers. They know what's going on. But they need leadership. They must be brought together. They must be given opportunities to discuss the history of these institutions, what we've tried, and what we should try now. And, as important as any group excepting the inmates themselves, there are workers at New Hope—attendants, teachers, psychologists, others—who would join us. I know, with absolute certainty, that there are people who are working there who are waiting for the right time, the right plan, the leadership to force an evacuation of that institution."

"Mike, I have some time put aside, time I was planning to use to finish a revision of my textbook. I think I'll delay that revision a bit longer. I don't feel much like writing now anyway; it's a good excuse. I think I'll be here next week for a couple of days and, possibly, the week after for a couple of days. I'll give you a call tonight after my return to Boston. Let me do some thinking. Maybe I can help."

# Chapter 16

## An Interaction

*Will these bodies go to sleep,*
*When dirt is thrown upon the heap?*
*Will they lose their skin and hair,*
*When Death's Angel removes the air?*

*Poor Willie's dead,*
*And like others in that place,*
*No one there to say a Mass,*
*Or shed a tear or stop for grace.*

*Will little Willie be more proud,*
*When he finds the silver cloud?*
*When his body goes to sleep,*
*Will the worms let it keep?*

*Poor Willie's dead,*
*But, then, so are the rest,*
*Willie, Schmidty, Adam Mack,*
*The good, the square, the best.*

*Can Wilile's leave remove our dread,*
*Unveil the sin of living death?*
*Will it expose this evil pose,*
*Where worms abound in life's repose?*

---

"Professor Edward, I've been thinking about some of the things you've been saying. As I get it, some of us here aren't getting a fair deal. Right?"

"Right."

"You think that some of us—all of us—could do much better on the outside. Even the low grades, the vegetables. Right?"

"Wrong. I'm talking about human beings—not vegetables."

"I'm sorry, Professor. You know what I mean."

"Yes, but you—not especially you, but you too—should not speak of people as if they are other than people. I'm sorry, Adam, I shouldn't lecture you."

"It's O.K., Professor, I understand. Really. And, I'm with you."

"I know. You understand more than most here whom I've been speaking with about these matters. But why? You've told me more than once that you're happy at New Hope. You've told me that folks get a good deal here. Why are you so interested in what I've been saying?

"I do get a fair shake. And I think most of the attendants and the docs are good guys. But every once in a while, I worry about things, and I think about the outside, and why I'm here while the whole world is on the outside. But, I'm here! Professor, I'm not dumb like some of the others here. I think a lot about things, and I figure out things good, maybe better than some of the attendants.

"Professor, I'm a human being. I want to live free. Maybe, maybe I might someday want to live outside, and have my own kids . . . and be part of a real family. Sometimes, I feel bad about being here. Sometimes, I almost cry, Professor."

"Do you want to help us, Adam? Is that what you're saying?"

"I don't know, Professor. Hey, gotta run now. Have to go to little Willie's funeral."

"Who's Willie?"

"Used to work at his dorm before I was shifted to Wallin Hall. Nice kid. Just dropped dead on Saturday. The doc in his building tol' me about it yesterday. That doc didn't even know Willie's last name, and he been the building doc for years. I'm going to the funeral, so there'll be one guy there who knew Willie, who knew he had a last name. I been to funerals here before. I go any time I know the kid. Like you say, a human being should expect that, when he goes, people'll pay their respects, people who knew him. So I try to go, and sometimes a few of the other guys around here come along too."

"Adam, you're a decent man. Is there anything that I could do?"

"What can you do? 'Cept, maybe you can get this shitty state to put some kind of a real marker on Willie's grave. You know what they use? They use numbers. He had a name. He had a real mom and dad once. And the state gives him a number. You seen the markers at the New Hope Cemetery, Professor?"

"Yes, I have, Adam. But God will find Willie anyway."

"Don't joke, Professor. Ain't no God for guys like Willie and me. God is for those on the outside."

"I wasn't joking. If there's a God for those on the outside, He will want to find Willie, and He knows about New Hope."

"Then, why would He keep us here? Why does that kid die? Why no markers? Why does Mr. Johnson sometimes beat the kids? Why this place?"

"God didn't make New Hope. Man did! I don't *really* know why, Adam. But as I live and breathe, I know that we must evacuate these hells—not for God, for people, for each of us."

"I like that word, Professor."

"What word?"

"Evacuate. It's a good word, and I know what it means."

# Chapter 17

## A Funeral Poem

Glorified and sanctified be God's great name.
Amen, amen, amen.
O God, full of compassion,
Grant perfect rest unto the soul of Willie,
What's his name?
Lord of mercy, bring him under the cover of
   Thy wings,
And let his soul be bound up,
In the bond of eternal life.
Amen.
Amen.

      Job's watching up there somewhere,
      Finally found that terrible land,
      Where his words come true again,
      Again and again for all those damned.

      Job's crying for his brothers,
      For sons and daughters,
      For fathers and mothers,
      For human flesh; for all the others,
      That makes his prophecy ring in our time.

Let that which causes the black day to
   terrify us.
Let the night be desolate.
Let the stars of the twilight be dark.

Why didn't I die in the womb, perish at birth?
Why did I, who long for death,
   Live?

Find the grave.
Turn me to dust.
Kill this already dead son.

We're the living dead,
But little Willie's died.
We are dead, but he's left us.
Willie's gone and he's alone.
And we are too,
Gone and alone.

It must be true that the agony of death is not the death but the dying, and the terror of death is neither the death nor the dying, but the living!

Little Willie's dead,
Just fell upon the dirt,
Never knew what hit him,
Mightn't even hurt.

Willie's dead and gone,
Just peeled off and dropped,
Popped something in his head,
And his heart just stopped.

Heard about the news,
While at a football game,
Called Doc at the school,
Who didn't know Willie's name.

Little Willie's dead,
Hardly a soul will cry,
And the biggest sadness in my heart,
Is not that Willie's died,
But hardly a soul will cry.

Little Willie's gone.
What's his name again?
Come hear the preacher say his words,
And comfort all his friends.

As death is more precise than life, it is less anxiety-ridden. As life is more ambiguous, it is less comprehensible. As death's personal relevance is no more than a fleeting moment, it need never be contended with. As its angel delivers the ultimate decree, the response is rarely "no," but always "why?" Its mystery is ultimately related to "when," not "if."

Little Willie's gone.
What's his name again?
Come, hear the preacher say some words,
To comfort all his friends.

As dying is not for the dead, neither is living for the live. As the dead have already died, the live are already living. As the dead are past dying, the live are past the "notion" of living.

> As not all lifes Live.
> So each one Alive is more than a Life.

Little Willie's gone. What's his name again? Read the paper about cuddly seals, if they only looked like crocodiles, and, if Willie were more the human being, or less, we wouldn't have this trouble, in comforting all his friends.

> Come read about the cuddly seals,
> Who weren't decent enough to be crocodiles.
> > The public has conquered and the danger
> > > is gone.
> > The burden is lifted and souls have been won.
> > In Boston, little and large old ladies
> > > will lay aside their tennis shoes.
> > While in Syracuse, men will breathe easier,
> > And women will return to household chores
> > > with stronger spines and softer smiles.
> > The seals will live, and long live the seals.
> > The baby, cuddly, snow-white seals will
> > > live until—
> > They live at least a month,
> > And until they turn brown,
> > And until they weigh eighty pounds,
> > And until they leave their mothers,
> > And until they are no longer as cute as
> > > they were.
> > When their time comes, the once-baby cuddly,
> > > snow-white seals will not be—
> > Clubbed to death,
> > > or
> > Skinned alive,
> > > or
> > Garroted.
> > When their time comes, these two- or three-
> > > month old brown animals will be shot:
> > With a modern clean rifle,
> > > or
> > With sleek and swift arrows.
> > And when their time comes, heed Prime
> > > Minister Trudeau's admonition:
> > "Those who protest won't be shown the same
> > > photograph of baby seals with their big
> > > blue or brown eyes."

And when their time comes, protect your
    government, complained Minister of
    Fisheries Davis, for:
"A lot of young people in distant countries
    now think of Canada only in terms of seals."

A lot of young people in distant countries
    now think of the U.S.A. only in terms
    of Vietnam, Chicago, Watergate, and Selma.

And legions of people in all lands have
    thought:
Of Germany, only in terms of Nazis,
Of Rome, only in terms of Lion Pits,
Of the U.S.S.R., only in terms of Cancer Wards,
Of Russia, only in terms of Czars,
Of Chamberlain, only in terms of "peace in
    our time,"
Of King John, only in terms of murder and
    deceit,
And, of Evil, only in terms of its ability
    to flood out Goodness.

Yet, the baby seals can lead mankind out
    of the wilderness.
And we can learn from them:
That evil thrives as a life is devalued,
That evil flourishes as it is rationalized,
That evil is man's unique gift to the universe.

And man will learn that he, and all men,
    are judged,
And judge by that which makes us less
    than men,
By that which we hate, not by that which
    we love,
By that which shames us, not by that which
    gladdens us.
By that which is in our hands, not by that
    which is in our hearts,
By that which makes man the animal, not by
    that which makes the animal man.

The antecedents of evil require a disregard
    for life,
As he who is selected for debasement *must*
    be judged a less equal being,
As consequently, he who so judges *must*
    be known for that judgment.

Little Willie's gone.
The funeral's over now.

The nonevent happened, but didn't need to, as the happening may have needed to, but shouldn't have, a nonentity is, but needn't be, as some of those (of us!) who lived these 50,000 years would be missed, will be missed.

> The only hope, our last last straw, is
>> that some will be missed.
> One man has value.
> He should have lived.

But, as the Minister Man said,
"Now, we have a friend, a lawyer, an advocate
  in heaven."
And, as the Minister Man's lady said,
"Willie's on a trip, like from the state school
  to the New Hope Mall."
As all were instructed to repeat,
"You have removed your contemptible body to
  heavenly rest."
Amen and hallelujah!
Amen, and convince the poor that rats are pets—
  better than dogs.
Amen, and tell the old ladies that seals
  are crocodiles.
Amen, and convince yourself that Willie's on
  a trip—
Just like downtown—
And when he gets there, we'll all have a new
  friend in heaven.
Amen and hallelujah!

———————————

# Chapter 18

## Sins of the Prophets

*10/8/72   Author's Diary*

### "A Short Prejudiced History"

In the beginning, humans were created, and then humans created the criteria for being human. In the beginning, such criteria were simple, so simple that criteria were not important. When no person had language, humans needed no language. When no person had tools, humans needed no tools. In the beginning, the mere emergence from a woman's belly made one human.

Then humans discovered their hands and their fingers. Subsequent discoveries led to the invention of laws, books, print, civilization, science, and attempts to control the environment.

During the interim, humans sought new understandings of themselves, their relationships with others, and with a higher being.

And all the while, criteria and new criteria were invented and stipulated, first to classify, then to separate and set aside; eventually— from time to time, later more than from time to time—to defile, to dehumanize, to murder.

People with special characteristics—the blind, the deaf, the retarded, the special for a time, or the special irrespective of time or culture—became consistent targets for those who would separate one human being from another.

And, with each separation, prophets would announce that solutions to problems were at hand. The light at the end of the tunnel would now shine brightly. Desperate and sick humans would now be saved.

The ancients had their solutions, not human but honest and without sham. Go, mother, take your sick child to the mountaintop; there the gods will decide who should live, who should die, who will be inscribed in the Book of Life or the Book of Final Decree.

So they went, some to the mountains, and the "Hansels and Gretels" to the forests. But our priests told us that God was not pleased. Go ye not to the mountains and the forests. Thou shalt not kill! We, the state, will take your child in our asylums. We will care for the sick, the mad, the idiot child that you have spawned and let loose in this cruel and hard world.

> Give us your child to minister to.
> Give us this forsaken being whom you have loved.
> Give us that progeny who has no future.
> God and the state will serve all beings.
> And, so, they came,
> From the farms and the villages,
> From the great and the weak,
> Innocent of the ways of priests and prophets.
> And the state kept its word,
> If not its faith,
> Kept its covenant,
> If not with God, then with the Devil.
> First hundreds,
> Then thousands,
> Then hundreds of thousands,
> Tomorrow, millions may inhabit our Hells on
>     this earth.

Again, certain prophets told the people that the God-state was not pleased with the work of these faithful servants. We must design new homes, humane homes, small homes, regional homes, halfway homes, group homes, normalized homes, unit homes, extended-care homes, but we must keep separate those who belong with us from those who do not. We must guarantee to every family who has a child with special needs that the family will be here and the child will be there. This is a Great American Dream.

In an earlier time, the state first created homes for the little children —the greenhorn children, the dirty children, and the waifs. And the state told those greenhorn parents, "You offend us with your foreign tongues, your strange smells, and peculiar habits. Give us your children and we will melt them down and, then, remake them as Americans. But if they do not learn our ways quickly enough, or if you refuse to encourage our ways in your houses, we will take your children. We will place them in better homes, foster homes, or orphan homes. We, the state, will try to do for your children what you could not do." And, so, the poor and immigrant were the first to be fooled and pulled and subdued. For isn't it written in the Book that God created man and woman to multiply and subdue the earth? And isn't the state commanded to subdue all men and women?

But what the state first created to enclose and control the poor— what the powerful and elite created for others—now consumes those very people who designed the system. First conceived to protect people of refinement, the system now remains to imprison their descendants. Irony of ironies, the state control, and the state hospital, and Camelot—its progenitors once known as the poorhouse, then the county home, now the convalescent home called Camelot—open their arms to the children, and grandchildren, and great-grandchildren of those who began the process that led to the destruction of family life and responsibility, once the very strength of our earliest settlers.

# Chapter 19

## Power to the Powerless

*10/10/72  Author's Diary*

### "On Power: A Faithful Tape Transcript of Edward's Class, First Ten Minutes, 10/5/72"

"What is power? How strong I am, or how strong you permit me to be? Can I exert my will over you if you refuse to permit it? Speaking hypothetically, if I told you—a graduate class—to read a book, write a paper, take an examination, anything, is there a law of nature (disregarding the university for the sake of argument, if not prudence) that requires you to accede to my request or, even, to my demand? If one is willing to pay any consequence, can one control another's will? That, my friends, is the issue that I would like to discuss with you today, that is, if you will permit it.

"Here is an example, a modest example, at least in Sweden if not here. I suspect that today, in our culture, it would be very unlikely for such examples to actually occur. One might even say such examples would deny the very fabric of our external reality.

"About two years ago, Bengt Nirje, former Secretary General of the Swedish National Parents' Association for Retarded Children, visited our campus. Amid all the official hellos and introductions, the formal addresses and colloquia, and the marvelous fellowship of good meals and drink together, a compelling theme emerged—anchored in the normalization principle. The simplicity of Bengt Nirje made it easy for us to explore with him the Swedish experience, more than that—the Swedish human ethos.

"We talked about being handicapped in Sweden, and we in this country began to understand a bit more the frontier rawness of our own culture. We learned that, although we have progressed millennia in technological and scientific areas, we have neglected our spiritual and humanistic—some would say 'civilizing'—development. We talked about the summer of 1968 in Sweden, when a group of home-owners in a small Swedish town protested the support of small community homes for adult retarded people in their neighborhood. The subsequent public debate demonstrated that, on the one hand, prejudice in Sweden still exists and, on the other hand, general public attitudes and moral indignation overwhelmingly reject such prejudice.

"We spoke with feeling, and on our parts, envy, about the normalization principle. This principle—so widely bandied about here in the United States and so superficially understood and, more strikingly, so easily rejected—simply means making available to the mentally retarded conditions of everyday life which approximate as closely as possible the norms and patterns of the mainstreams of society. We discussed the elements of a normal rhythm of the day, of a normal routine of the week, of what it means to live as a normal human being. We enumerated the particulars of normal living:

"Retarded adults should not be required to live on the same premises as retarded children. Work in sheltered workshops or within institutions should be paid for. Residential facilities should be in community settings and not isolated from ordinary society. Living environments should allow for privacy and a sense of personal dignity. People should not be required to work or attend school in the same facility where they live. Everyone is entitled to pocket money.

"We spoke about important matters and trivial ones, grand ideas and silly notions, and even the yet-unresolved problems Sweden now confronts. There are no utopias in this world, but it is equally clear that there are places where people can live as human beings irrespective of their capacities or potentials for contribution to the larger society.

"What may have impressed us the most was a statement of beliefs, questions, and demands prepared by a group of fifty young adults—all mentally retarded—who met in Malmö, Sweden, on May 8 to 10, 1970, to review their current opportunities and to conceptualize (yes, conceptualize) their unmet needs. The Swedish Parents' Association in 1968 sponsored the first such national conference of young adults. This second conference illuminated for us, in a way which we were unable to understand heretofore, the extraordinary progress accomplished in Sweden on behalf of (and by) the mentally retarded—in more profound ways, on behalf of all humanity.

"The reformation in Sweden is not complete. Bengt Nirje is no longer Secretary General of the Parents' Association for Retarded Children. Possibly, even Sweden (or the Parents' Association) is not ready to seriously consider the real demands of victims. Possibly, even in Sweden, prices must be paid for those who insist on the reform of government or human-welfare systems. However, it was clear to each of us who participated with Bengt Nirje during those two days that, while Sweden must continue its reform, we in the United States must begin our revolution."

# Chapter 20

## Who Has the Final Option?
## A Classroom Discussion

"Professor, you claim that these institutional inmates can make demands, can intrude their demands into this insensitive society."

"Correct, John."

"Impossible. It can't work. They're retarded. Certainly, they can have conferences and draw up lists of grievances. But there is a paradox here. The establishment has options; it, too, doesn't have to listen. The list will be discarded if the authorities don't agree with its contents."

"You're right. Authorities don't have to respond. But, then, even institutional inmates, as you put it, have the next option—to continue their demands. In the end, anyone has the final option—including an inmate—given that he is willing to pay any price, even extermination."

"Professor Edward, I just realized that power isn't taken. It's given."

"Yes."

"Then, one way to define a powerful person is the degree to which he persuades others to give him power."

"That's a way, John."

"Another way is the degree to which he causes others to act."

"That, too, is a way, Steve."

"Another is how he influences people."

"I agree."

"Then, power is not actually defined in terms of one's objective physical or psychological energy but, essentially, in terms of ability to control and influence."

"Yes."

"Like love, power isn't taken, it's given."

"That's what we seem to be saying."

"But are people strong enough to resist attempts to control them? Skinner says all human beings live controlled lives."

"Even on Skinner's terms, if reinforcers can be revealed that persuade people—for example, inmates—to resist their institutional control, they will deny others that power in favor of another source of controllers, whatever that may be."

"O.K., Professor, you have suggested that if inmates are convinced, for whatever reasons, to deny their keepers control over them, there is no way the keepers can continue to dominate them."

"Exactly. Again, however, given the condition that the inmates become convinced that they should pay *any* price to achieve the goal."

"Professor, how can we test the hypothesis?"

"Well, one way is to consider the possibilities and dangers of a program that operationalizes what you term 'the hypothesis.' "

"What do you mean?"

"We could help the inmates here gain the independence that is the inherent right of each human being."

"You're suggesting . . ."

"That, since the professionals, the state, even reformers, have been unwilling or unable to secure essential rights for these inmates, it is possible that such rights may better be achieved by those who are the victims. Not only are they the victims, but also in matters such as this, each human being creates and shapes his own destiny. As I cannot seize power over you, in the same way, I cannot give you freedom."

"My God. What an unthinkable thought."

"But it does have a special fascination . . . no?"

# Chapter 21

## A Brief Interaction

"Professor, do you have time to talk?"

"Sure, Don, want a cup of coffee? What's up?"

"Thanks, it's about yesterday's class, our discussion on power. I'm puzzled. Was it just academic talk, or do you have a plan that we're not in on?"

"Tell me what you think I have in mind."

"In a nutshell, I believe you're actually advocating some kind of revolution at New Hope, one led by the inmates."

"What would you advocate, Don? You've been to New Hope. You've seen the conditions. You've heard and smelled and felt what others have. You've been shocked, offended, angry, possibly desperate—as have many others. You've observed parents, professionals, distinguished citizens attempt to rectify the evils of New Hope. You have worked with your classmates and alone—valiantly, sometimes effectively—to right wrongs, to help, even if with temporary solutions. What has been accomplished from all of this enormous energy, dedication, anguish? I'll tell you! Nothing."

"I know. I know. But, what can inmates accomplish that none of us was able to accomplish? You, Professor Edward, are an important man. You've written books, lectured, been a leader in this field for many years. What have you done?"

"Frankly, very little, and that's the point."

"You aren't responsible for the horrendous state of affairs we're in. Yet, quite bluntly, you haven't helped much. In the four years you've been at the university, the county and commonwealth have jointly constructed a new mental hospital at a cost of $25 million dollars. And now, New Hope is considering tearing down the entire place—*and starting all over again with a new, much larger state school!*

"Is that progress, Professor? Would you claim credit for those developments? Obviously, you would not! Obviously, you have had little—at least little positive—influence insofar as the encouragement of alternatives to institutionalization is concerned."

"Exactly. Please excuse the pedantic tone, but I think the time has come for people to consider the possibility that each man reflects and must determine his own destiny. Who are most directly affected by the policies practiced at New Hope? The inmates and, next, the attendant staff—not the professionals, not even the parents. Who have most to gain and most to lose as New Hope swings from good to bad to terrible? The inmates and that staff. Who should be willing to risk everything, to pay any price in an effort to change the place? Theoretically, first the inmates, then the attendant staff."

"Or, at least, enough of the inmates and, at the beginning, some of the staff."

"Right on!"

"Good luck, Professor. I want to wish you the best."

"What do you mean, 'Good luck?' When you were ignorant of this idea, it was impossible for you to get involved. Now, you cannot be uninvolved. Whatever you decide, you are a part of this thinking. Do nothing, walk away, and you have consciously turned away from participation. You are as involved as I."

"I'm not. I can't be. I sympathize, you know I do."

"Not enough. C'mon, Don, you do have a commitment with us, don't you? Afraid to lose your intellectual virginity?"

"Goddamn it, who are you to tell me how to spend my life and where to make my commitments? Sorry, Professor, I shouldn't have said that."

"Yes, you should. And I have an answer for you. I have the same responsibility to you that you have to me in this regard. The one thing each of us can bring to our relationship is honesty. I am responsible for being honest with you, saying exactly what I think in matters of mutual interest and concern. With your original question, I took on certain responsibilities. And so did you. Now, you have the option to tell me to bug off. O.K. But you can't tell me that an honest opinion in a matter of mutual concern is out of the bounds of friendship, good taste, professorial-student relationships, you name it. I think that you are now involved, whatever you decide. We can't erase the past half-hour, as much as we might like to at this point.

"Don, you're a good guy, and I've had a tough day. I guess I did shoot from the hip. Well, the hip and I apologize. Let's forget it for now. I'm tired, really."

"Professor, you don't understand. I want to help. I will in my way. But I'm a private person."

"I do understand, Don."

# Chapter 22

## A Private Person

Don Baldwin is a private person. A good person, decent, concerned. Don radiates, with a laugh, a warmth, a response, a man who knows how to encourage others—both by what he says and because of what he is. Don Baldwin is a very good student, a conceptualizer, creative, a leader who can follow. He is alive, alive, alive—but a private person.

Don Baldwin has seen and experienced too much to be a pessimist. A war does things to a man. Since his return, and his marriage, he has never flinched and has always accepted his share of the dirt and drudgery. He's served the state school as a volunteer, clinical student, once as a part-time summer employee. During his years, he has seen more than most men would bear. But, in adversity, he appears to grow stronger and wiser. And we should seek his council and hear him.

We might imagine what this private man would say if we could but read his mind:

> I have confronted the foul,
>    and we are all people.
> I have been to the bottom,
>    and it is part of the human continuum.
> When appearances tell you that nothing remains,
>    you either die or become an optimist.
>
> Optimism is not
>    in believing that things will turn out
>    well, objectively—
> But, in believing that one can face things,
>    subjectively, however they turn out.
> Optimism is not in feeling good—

but, in feeling that good has a chance
to survive.
Optimism flows not from defeats,
    bitterness, or victories and joys, of the past—
But, in being here now,
    knowing that the past has strengthened you.

How does he struggle with a decision he must make, knowing that he is as puzzled about the question posed as the answer eventually to be provided? What are his thoughts during the early dawn, when the world is quiet and one still has hope?

If God is on your side, you die in your own bed,
You own a bed,
One you bought.
It's your life!

If God is on your side, you own your body.
You take it where you please;
You do with it as you please;
You may even destroy it if you please.

If God is on your side, the state doesn't own you;
It hardly knows you,
And it hardly cares.
But you care that it hardly cares!

If God is on your side, you have a friend,
One to whom you speak the truth,
As he speaks the truth to you,
One who restores your faith in man.

If God is on your side, the world makes sense,
The deluge is contained,
The present is not too painful,
And the design for each of us holds nothing but good.

If God is on your side, you have faith.

"I am a private person, but. . . . In this time, it is difficult for a man with such inclinations to be, truly, a private person. For a man to have regard for his own privacy, he must have feelings about such matters as individual conscience, liberty, and opportunity to make choices.

"In this time, it is difficult for the private person to secure his personal environment while great segments of society are in either physical or ideological enslavement. For the private person knows that privacy surrounded by public derogation is less privacy than isolation, less self-determination than self-concealment, and less creating one's own pristine life than fleeing an ugly reality.

"In this time, the truly private person knows that his privacy will not be secured until all people are free; his affairs will not be closed to all but

**104**

himself until all of society's affairs and institutions are open to everyone. Essentially, one's private life must depend on everyone else's public lives. "In this time, it is difficult for a man to lead a truly private life."

And, if we were to observe Don Baldwin, inside and outside, during those moments, we might conclude that:

Each creative mind records the essence that
makes man unique.
Each truth is the wisdom of all of the past
and all of the future.
Each courageous commitment reveals the depth
and strength of all people.
Each act of love symbolizes man's potential.
Each man's decision to assume personal
responsibility to mankind begins his new life.

\* \* \*

And, eventually, Don Baldwin made his decision.

# Chapter 23

## The Architects

"We'll build a new homelike state school, a better state school, a magnificent state school. The critics are right. This ugly old school is a disgrace. Government must do more for these, the least of our citizens. Brick by brick, we will tear down New Hope."

"And build a new New Hope but the same New Hope. You may try, but you will fail to simulate home and family because our society has given up on real homes and families for these inmates. You would substitute the Bastille and attendants for home and family."

"C'mon Professor, be reasonable. This is our chance to make a great contribution to human welfare."

"And to architects and bankers and contractors."

"That remark is in poor taste."

"But is it untrue?"

"You're insulting, Professor!"

"Mr. Slade, I was asked to serve on this State Advisory Planning and Construction Council. I have heard a great deal about the construction you hope to begin. But, where is the planning? What will be different at New Hope? Frankly, if you had accomplished anything for me this afternoon, it was to convince me that the state has embarked on an almost criminal policy in its unquenchable desire to build more and more state schools—when we have too many today. One state school in a civilized society is one too many. And, Mr. Slade, you and your firm, frankly, are not without some responsibility in this crime—not that I blame you completely. You're in business and want to sell construction. Indelicately put, you're a high-class whore. I assume your six percent fee comes to a very tidy sum of money."

"You're an outrage! I never mentioned fees or profits. Those considerations are unimportant. By the easily proven fact that we never, never, discuss such matters, it is clear to any but the most biased person that fees and profits do not influence us insofar as the professional aspects of our work are concerned."

"Excuse the analogy, but you don't have to talk about, or with, Jesus for him to have influenced you."

"Mr. Chairman, I don't—nor does the firm of Bullock, Price, King—have to tolerate this man's insane diatribe. Next, he'll equate us with Albert Speer."

"Interesting reaction, Mr. Slade. Do you have a conscience?"

"This is outrageous. We are leaving!"

"Mr. Slade, Dr. Edward, please! This unfortunate exchange is very disturbing. I beg both of you gentlemen to control yourselves—especially you, Dr. Edward—so we may continue the meeting. Please, Mr. Slade, we must make some decisions today. I ask you to remain. Please."

"Very well, Mr. Guild. Out of respect to you and this council we will remain. But, remember, we have a right to be protected from Dr. Edward's slanderous and unfair remarks."

"Mr. Slade, will you overview the plan for the new state school?"

"And we do have a plan! The new school will house 2400 residents, approximately the same number as currently. However, there will be many striking differences between the old and new school. First, no resident, excepting the most severely retarded, will be forced to sleep with more than three others in the same room. Some bedrooms will be for only two residents. Except for the severely retarded, each residential building will have its own integrity and relative independence as an environmental setting. Each will contain four units, six beds to each unit, and living-day room, kitchen-dining room, mud room, and play-recreation room in the basement. Such buildings will be furnished with appropriate equipment and coordinated colors and textures for the particular group to be served. Any questions at this point?"

"Mr. Edward remarked that you haven't yet developed the total program. Shouldn't such work be accomplished before you design this new facility, even if the program plan is very general, and no doubt pro tem?"

"Certainly, Mrs. Finkel. And we are developing a training curriculum and a building-usage guide. In fact, I serve on the state school committee that meets regularly and conscientiously to define goals and means. I can report to you that the Goals and Means Committee will have its report to this council within the next two or three months."

"Is that before or after we are to approve your construction plan, Mr. Slade?"

"You know the answer to that one, Professor. You know that I would have preferred that we had such plans before we designed the facility. But professionals just don't work on a reasonable schedule, and we had to move ahead. May I remind this group that if we don't receive your approval very soon—essentially, at this meeting—to progress from line drawings to more detailed schematics, the state will lose 2 million dollars in federal construction funds under the provisions of the Mental Retardation Facilities and Community Mental Health Centers Construction Act."

"I didn't actually hear your answer, Mr. Slade, before or after?"

"After."

"Mr. Slade, will windows be at eye level?"

"Yes, in many, but not in all buildings. There are places and groups that demand greater precautionary measures than others within the institution."

"Will all windows be clear?"

"Some of the residential units for our most severely retarded will have quite attractive, I think, glass-brick wall sections that will substitute for more conventional windows."

"Why?"

"The reason is quite obvious, I think. Severely retarded residents would break more ordinary windows. Besides, we don't believe that seeing the outside environment is quite as important for that group."

"Oh?"

"Well, please Mr. Myron, don't misunderstand. I am speaking only in relative terms. Our essential interest is to develop the most humanizing and normalizing environments for all of our residents. But, although that is the major goal, we must be realistic."

"Speaking of being realistic, how much will this new facility cost the taxpayers?"

"Professor, I have heard you on this subject before and was expecting the question. Exclusive of land costs, the new state school will come in at slightly over 108 million dollars—today's costs, of course. The longer we wait, the more expensive the construction becomes."

"Therefore, at today's costs, the new state school will require $45,000 for every resident admitted, no doubt more, and not including interest payable to bondholders, the purchase of land and the demolition costs for leveling the present state school."

"Correct, but these costs include all other site work fees, and all general new equipment."

"Professor Edward, how much interest will accrue to bondholders?"

"For this project, approximately 100 million dollars; insofar as the state's current 613 million dollar mental health construction program, 600 million taxfree dollars will be earned by banks and their bondholders. Mrs. Wein, one should also mention that the state must 'back' these bonds, or the state's credit will be seriously impaired."

"Of what significance is that, Professor?"

"Great significance! For example, even if the state decided in ten years to evacuate New Hope, it would be almost impossible to follow through with such a plan. As long as New Hope has inmates, and as long as families or Medicare in the state pay their keep and, thus, the bonding obligations, those who 'invested' in the institution will receive payments on the notes they hold. Evacuate New Hope, and the other New Hopes, and we will either have to pay off possibly billions to bondholders or force the Housing Finance Agency to default on their payments. The state can legally do the latter, but it would no doubt cause a severe governmental crisis. The Housing Finance Agency has never defaulted to its bondholders, hence the relatively low interest on such bonds."

"My God, people, we are stuck, and each time we build another institution we almost guarantee that more generations to come will be required to live in these places."

"Yes, Ina, this is one reason why many of us have been tormented in the face of state policy and utter indifference to this bonding issue, and many other issues as equally serious or more so. But, Mr. Slade, to return to New Hope, you mentioned that the severely retarded will not be assigned to small bedrooms. How large will their dormitories be?"

"As small as twenty beds, with one large dormitory of sixty beds. But, you must understand that most of the mildly and moderately retarded will be assigned to the aforementioned small bedrooms."

"But, Mr. Slade, most of the new admissions have been severely retarded and, further, such admissions will increase, not decrease. There is little doubt that, in a decade or so, practically every resident of the state school will be severely retarded and multiply handicapped or disturbed—with but a relative handful who will be moderately retarded."

"That appears to be true; however, we must plan for our current population. We must not forsake them in the interests of whatever the future may or may not dictate. Our interest as architects is in designing a facility that America can be proud of, that will exemplify the human motives that are embedded in the American dream."

"Mr. Slade, I could vomit. For many, *the* American dream is 20 million blacks swimming back to Africa with a handicapped person under one arm and an elderly person under the other."

"Mr. Edward!"

"I apologize. Let's go on. What about toilets? Privacy? Toilet seats?"

"There will be toilet seats on all toilets, with the exception of those in dormitories for the severely retarded. Needless to say, we deeply regret having had to make that decision. However, you know as well as I that toilet seats in those dormitories would be ripped off in a matter of hours or days. We have had experiences."

"What about privacy in the toilets? Doors?"

"It was disallowed, not approved, by the superintendent. We asked for doors, but he is worried about masturbation and homosexuality, maybe other things."

"So what else is new?"

"I beg your pardon?"

"If a state school segregates males and females, what would one expect but masturbation and homosexuality? The one thing these institutions consistently cure is heterosexuality."

"Let's not get into that, Professor Edward. New Hope is still trying to recover from the Gunn mess."

"Mr. Chairman, that is just the point. We are supposed to be planning a state school, but we are not planning; we are building. We are not thinking; we are acting. We are doing something instead of trying to comprehend our history, our problems, and our hopes for these residents—and, for that matter, our hopes for ourselves and for all human beings. We are trying to do something for people; yes, there is good will involved, I am sure. However, good will isn't enough; we must wrestle with questions that concern the definition of humanity, what people are entitled to because they are human beings, what survival means in terms of human beings. We must struggle with a conceptualization of a human being that is different from current conceptualizations. We must deal with a better understanding of human potential, human educability.

"Sorry, Mr. Chairman, let's proceed. I will try to control—if I can—the polemics."

"Professor Edward, why is there this enormous dissonance between the state perspective—the architects', among others—and yours? As you said, there is a degree of goodwill involved. At least, you haven't suggested that the state officials, and most of us here, are evil or mendacious people; and, on the other hand, you and your confederates have not co-opted all of virtue and truth."

"Dr. White, I have great admiration for your work and for you personally. I have enjoyed my participation on this council because of so many here who have permitted me to learn from them. There is no doubt that, insofar as their virtue and integrity are concerned, my colleagues on this committee need little admonition, especially from me."

"Then what are you trying to say?"

"That government and their agents, that committees such as ours—with the best of motivations—can make incredible errors when they seek to judge the needs and aspirations of other human beings."

"Such as?"

"That's easy; such as our statewide facilities construction program. However, permit me to attempt to respond to your other question, an attempt that requires some rather significant presumption on my part and, probably, forbearance on yours. Why? Why the dissonance? Why the gulf? Why, if we all mean to do good things for people?

"Simply stated, the state has different agendas, different priorities, different needs than individuals. Commissioners of mental health aren't necessarily less concerned about inmate welfare than, for example, nonprofessionals; they have different concerns and different responsibilities. For whatever reasons, and I wouldn't be so foolish as to attempt to analyze them, the state seeks to control, to supervise, to account for, to congregate together those who deviate from society's norms. The individual seeks to be included, to be a part of normal society, in spite of whatever deviancy he presents, in spite of the sometimes considerable discomfort or expense his inclusion may incur. Hence, the basic discrepancy between governmental and individual objectives. Add to this the exacerbation and convolution of the problem because, as we must try to remember, governments and agencies and committees are constituted by individuals and led by individuals. We contrive the disasters that cause our later suffering when we attempt to deal with them. However, and here is the essential difficulty, such problems are nearly always created for other people, never for those who design or administer the policies that spawn them. Consequently, commissioners execute programs that deprive other people of their liberty—while they not only enjoy their own freedoms but also gain, through the rewards and prestige of their positions, even greater opportunities for personal self-determination. Similarly, architects design institutions that, literally, imprison the inmates and, with the rewards of that work, create free and open environments for their own families. Or, for example, you can examine public and private day schools. From the schoolman's perspective, segregated classes for the mentally retarded are more manageable than integrated classes, possibly more economical, and certainly more visible, the last a not unimportant consideration in these days of accountability, taxpayer revolts, and the like. From the parents' perspective, they hope that their child with special needs can be properly educated in an integrated setting that will also provide for his particular requirements.

"So the discrepancy."

"Very enlightening, Professor. Thank you. Mrs. Frazier, I see you have a comment."

"Mr. Slade, I've heard a lot about tile walls, terrazzo floors, other institutional surfaces that contribute to the 'institutional look.' Will New Hope be spared tile halls and day rooms and cold terrazzo floors?"

"Not exactly, Mrs. Frazier. We believe that New Hope will have a great deal less of the so-called 'institutional look' and more wood surfaces, more carpeting, more color and texture. But, let's face it again, with incontinent and destructive patients, we can't expect the attendants to double their work to please our aesthetic needs. Tile and terrazzo are functionally superior materials in dormitories for the severely mentally retarded."

"Just how many of the total 2400 beds will be included in the larger, traditional, institutional dormitories?"

"Well, as you remember the Professor's comments, most of our new admissions to New Hope are now severely retarded, and this situation, if anything, will escalate in the coming years. We are planning for 2000 beds in the larger dormitories for the severely mentally retarded and 400 beds in the smaller cottages."

"Then, you are really building just another traditional institution, aren't you?"

"Not really. Even our large units are smaller than others in this state. We have tried not to compromise certain essential principles of normalization, but we have had to compromise on some issues. Remember, there are state building, fire, safety, and health codes. There are many third-party codes, for example, Medicare and Medicaid. If we do not abide strictly by these, the state will not be reimbursed for otherwise eligible residents. Further, we have to work with the present administration and staff. In the last analysis, they will have to live in these buildings. They, too, must be satisfied."

"I notice, Mr. Slade, that all dormitories are multistoried. How will residents in wheelchairs be transported outdoors? There are no provisions for elevators, are there?"

"No, but we have recommended in the initial program description that every effort be made to encourage attendants to transport bed patients and wheelchair residents outside, to take advantage of the lawns we are planning and the programs in other buildings."

"How will they do this?"

"Well, I guess they will have to carry the bed patients and wheel-chair patients out."

"And those on the second floor will be carried down, and later up, the stairs?"

"Yes, it will be difficult, but dedicated people can accomplish miracles."

"Such as the rectification of absolutely stupid architectural decisions? Mr. Slade, you are the quintessential hypocrite."

"Edward, damn you, virtue is no more an operating principle in your university than in my architectural firm."

"Let's not dodge behind your firm or my university. You may be right, you may be wrong. But let's talk about us—Slade and Edward. I don't confuse virtue with avarice. I can't claim that I'm less greedy than you—although, I hope I am—but I know the difference between greed and altruism. You don't!

"I had just been thinking that people who are locked up appear so much less human than people who are free. And then I hear about the deliberate planning of environments that cage people. For many at New Hope, the second floor will be a continuous isolation room or—what do they call it now?—a "time out" room. You do sound a bit like Albert Speer, Mr. Slade. I'm sorry if you are hurt, but not as sorry as I would be if you were not offended. At least you understand me, and you realize my disgust for what you and this state are doing, and what this council will undoubtedly endorse here today. When you discuss these matters, you should better meet at New Hope State School or at Brook Island. But, I suspect, that would be too much like bringing coals to Newcastle, even too much for your stomach, Mr. Slade. I also suspect that I should leave it to all of you here to find the most appropriate words and names to describe the activities of this group. The only name that leaps to view in my mind's eye is Draco of Athens. Good day, ladies and gentlemen! I resign from this council! Extend my regrets to the governor."

# Chapter 24

## Questions and Answers

### "Beds and Sex"

Thank Hell,
You bet your ass!
For sickly smells,
And urine gas.

Just beds and sex,
And things you dread,
An evil hex,
Whammo! you're dead.

Along a row,
I saw my bed,
Another blow,
Inside my head.

Tisket tasket,
Let's have some sex.
But Matron's a bastard.
He's by the bed.

One old lady sits on a stone.
She doesn't say "yes."
She doesn't say "no."
Now what do I do with this bone?

Mary had a little lamb.
In this damn place she could.
And, everywhere that lamb was rammed,
The boys all drooled and shook.

Little Jack sat in his corner,
And you know what he'd do.
Pulled on his horner,
Because he couldn't screw.

Beds and sex.
And lovin' too,
Could be the best,
But here we're screwed.

"Professor, could you clear something up? Why were all the trees cut and most of the plants and hedges removed from the New Hope campus?"

"I'll try and explain, but you may not believe me. About one year ago, Professor Gunn of the College of Human Development proposed that, for young children and adults, dormitories be made coeducational. As a few of you probably remember, the administration had been concerned—frightened is the word—because of the rather widespread homosexual activities in this institution. Gunn proposed a plan that would considerably increase heterosexual contacts and, hopefully, reduce homosexuality. Subsequently, a number of residents were reassigned to newly organized coed dorms. Dances and other social activities were sponsored, and attendants were encouraged to plan mixed-sex activities. For reasons dealing with general problems that many adolescents have, and the special problem menstruation creates among some young girls, teenagers were excluded from this new program. However, essentially, for all other residents an entirely new opportunity presented itself—spawning in the mainstream, so to speak."

"But what does this have to do with the flora and, I guess, the fauna?"

"Everything. The inmates took full advantage of this opportunity. Homosexuality appeared to decrease remarkably, but heterosexual activities increased even more remarkably."

"Professor, the flora . . ."

"The flora, oh yes. Where do you think these activities were conducted? The dorms continued to be policed. Consequently, the bushes were discovered and put to their historic usage. A few women became pregnant and, eventually, the administration met in an emergency session to deal with this new problem. I guess they learned that, while the conventional institution 'cures' but one thing—hererosexuality— the promotion of genuine reform is not without its problems. New Hope learned that they can't have it both ways. But, they wanted it both ways; hence, the defoliation. Obviously, if the inmates fornicated behind the bushes, the solution to the problem was to tear down the bushes and cut the trees. Ergo, there would no longer be any problem! But the problem wasn't solved. The trees were cut, and the institution began to take on the appearance of a battlefield. However, as you know, the University Ecology Society recently won a court order restraining the state from further defoliating the institutional grounds. What happens now is anyone's guess. The comic absurdity of it all is just too much for most ordinary people to believe—much less understand. By the way, the fornication continues, and some people claim that much of the enthusiasm for this activity is provided by several young male attendants. Who can comprehend all of this?"

"I don't comprehend it, nor do I believe it."

"Sorry, Marge. It's the truth. I can't help you believe something as bizarre as this, but it is the truth. It really happened. Understand it and you understand the state, and mental health, and institutions."

"What can we do?"

"Fight."

"How?"

"I have a plan. Permit me to explain it to you in detail."

---

*Mike Edward had a plan, a plan for today, for now. He wasn't interested in a plan for the future or study of the future. In his experience, he had found that the future has a way of delaying what can be accomplished today.*

*The future delays the present,*
*As the present beclouds it,*
*For planning the next move,*
*Gives reason to deny today's affairs.*

*We see studies and more studies,*
*That are not taken seriously,*
*As we attempt to predict the future,*
*To avoid the present.*

*Beware of Herman Kahn,*
*And crystal balls,*
*And institutes for the future,*
*And Ouija boards.*

*Deal with today,*
*With what we have learned,*

116

*Using the here,*
*For us now.*

*The future will unfold,*
*And if we do our homework,*
*And pay our dues,*
*The future holds nothing but good.*

# Chapter 25

## Return to Purgatory

And so it happened that a professor—Michael Steven Edward, a rather decent man, yet thought by a few who did not know him to be the reincarnation of de Sade with a bitter pen—and a few students, Don Baldwin among them, began the fermentation of a revolution at New Hope State School; a revolution that might eventually be led by inmates. Recruiting more students and others on the outside, they planned a general strategy that would encourage the leadership of insiders—whoever they might be. But, most essentially, it would include inmates themselves.

The plan was as uncomplicated as they could make it. Time was very short; Mike and Derrick TePaske and Judith Cohen, volunteers at New Hope, would return to several of the institutions visited six years earlier to take those once-famous or once-infamous—you be the judge—pictures. Again, they would attempt to record back ward life as seen through their eyes and through Derrick's camera. They would concentrate on some of the wards visited before. And they would try to answer a simple question:

> We have been faithful, glorious state.
> You are our hope.
> We are your servants.
> You are our master.
> We obey.
> You command.
> We have a question.
> You have the answer.

Six years,
72 months,
2160 days,
52,560 hours,
What have you done to relieve our suffering?

We are the faithful.
We are the forsaken.
We are the loving.
We are the unloved.

We are the trusting.
We are the untrustworthy.

We own nothing,
While you own us.

Let us look together,
At the holocaust,
At Purgatory,
At Pandemonium,
At what you have wrought.

What have you, glorious state, done,
To relieve our suffering,
To reduce the pain,
To soothe the anguish,
To heal our wounds,
To help us become human again?

Let us look together.
And, if you have forsaken us,
We will no longer be your servants.
We will leave these places.

We will trust in God,
Or, in ordinary people.
But, never again will we trust you,
While we chant:
    God, damn this Monolith,
    For what it does,
    To human beings.

And, what have you, the professionals, done,
As our protectors,
As our teachers,
As our benefactors,
As our brothers?

We will trust in God,

Or, in ordinary people.
But, most of all,
We will trust ourselves.

We are our advocates.
We will shape our destinies,
Our futures.
We will design tomorrow.

We will demand,
While you must beg our forgiveness.
For what you have done.
Which is both question and answer.

# Chapter 26

## Days of Darkness–Nights of Faith

The pictures were taken in this year of our Lord, 1972. Here is the evidence. The book is open. The truth is told, once again, hopefully more compelling than the last time. The professionals will see and compare; they will review their capabilities to help us! The administration will see and compare; they will account for their efforts on behalf of people. The legislators will see and compare; they must justify the money, the buildings, the laws, the regulations. Ordinary people will see and compare; they will search their roots, their humanity, their love, their very existence, while inmates suffer on their account. And, the inmates themselves will see and compare; they will consult and judge and reason. They will decide what must be done. They will seize this time and place for themselves and the work that they, and only they, can accomplish.

The inmates will act, or no one will act. The inmates will act on their own behalf, and on behalf of all people who know the difference between a human being and all other living things. The inmates will lead humanity out of hell.

There have been many photos and essayists, from Mike's *Hell's Capital* to his *Lives in Scape*, from Geraldo Rivera to Larry Brown, from *The Village Voice*, to the Springfield, Massachusetts newspapers, from Dorothea Dix to Phillip Wakstein. There have been advocates from William Bronston to Ben Ricci, from Wolf Wolfensberger to Gunnar Dybwad, from Judge Bazelon to Judge Ford. There have been many victims, from Nancy Beth Bowman to Adrianne Renelli. But to this date, has anyone put it all together?

Have the victims and the advocates coalesced on interests and issues? Are the photographs shared with those who are photographed, both victims and victimizers? Have we arranged for the necessary confrontations?

The following photos—products of real visits and live observations —and the verbal interchanges that subsequently swirled around them, involved the principal constituencies in the institutional drama. And, for some, it all became extensions of their very lives. What institutions were visited, how Mike outmaneuvered the gatekeepers, how these impossible tasks were made possible, need not be told to reveal the story. Is it not enough to say that—although time itself is finite, though some may disagree—a perspective on time is relative and bound to values and judgments? Isn't it enough to add that finite time moves infinitely? Possibly all one should expect from a storyteller is to be offered a sense of time and a relationship of one event to another.

O.K., my hands are clean; the excuses are in. Who could fault the writer for not being able to explain the details of strange or puzzling events? But do you want to know the truth, the way I feel now, as this pen moves from word to word, creating lines and pages and, eventually, this story? I feel dumb. I feel lazy. I feel that I've let you down. Why can't I construct a story, a cover, some explanation that rings true? Because it wouldn't be true; because I just don't know how all of these matters were accomplished so quickly, so suddenly. And I've decided within myself that, if a choice must be made, stupidity is preferable to dishonesty! The writer may survive the former—if he's lucky and if the reader is charitable—but never the latter, nor should he.

So, forgive my inadequacies, if you can, and examine these pictures, all true, all authentic, all recent, all part of this story.

Examine how some lives are lived during these times.

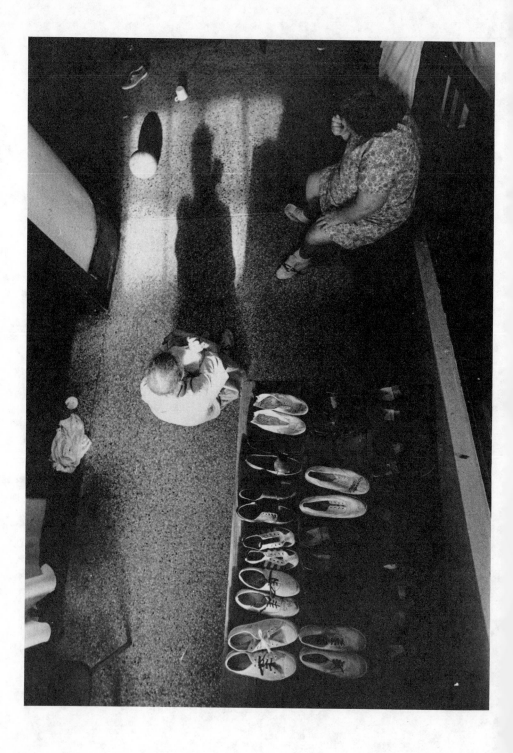

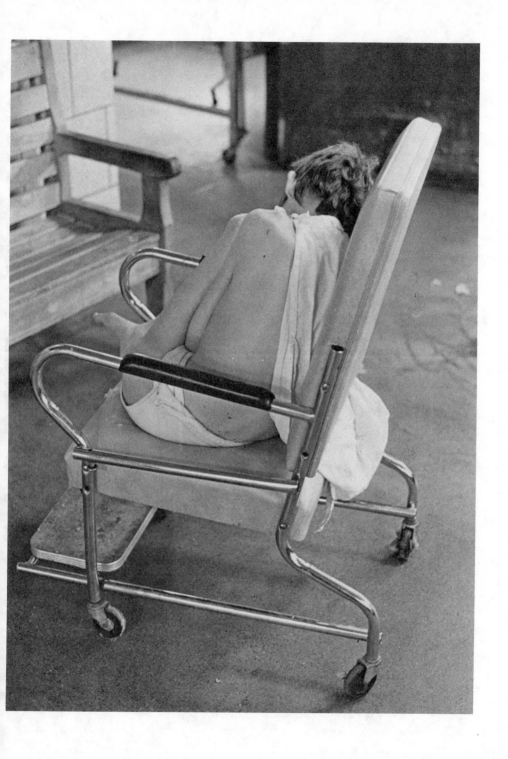

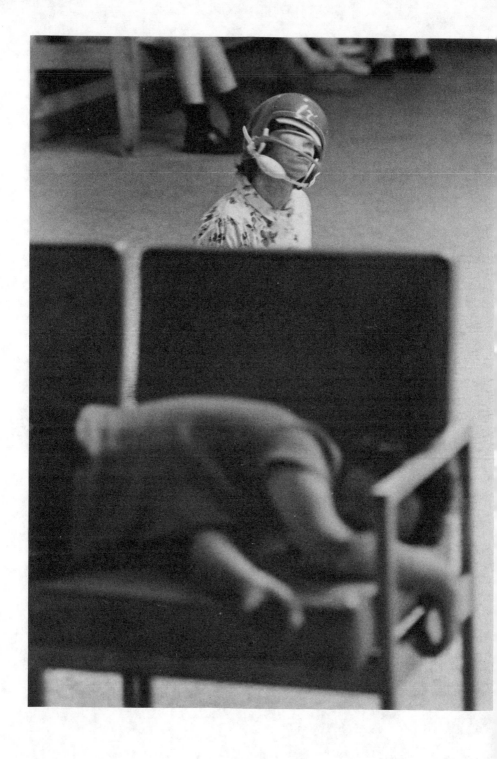

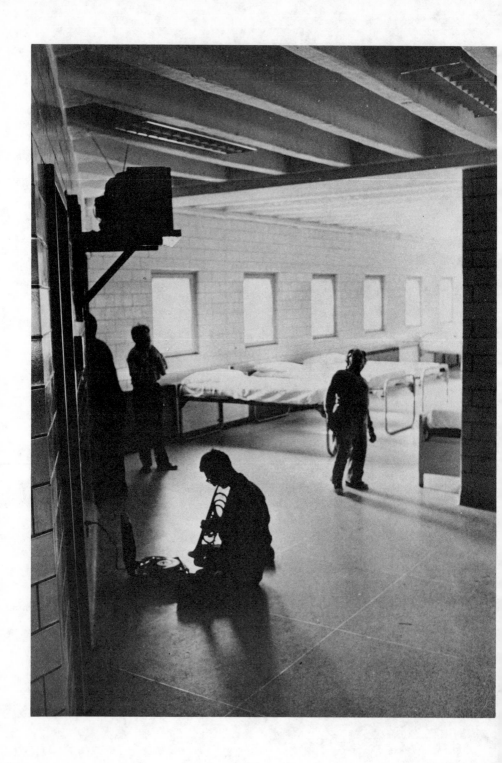

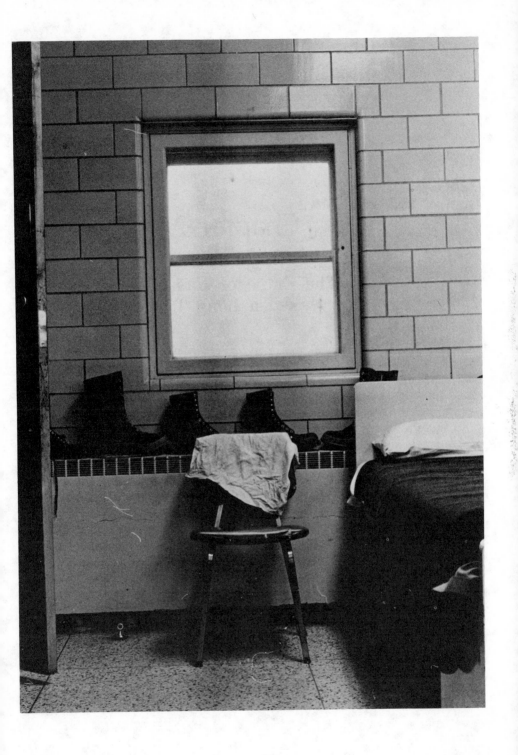

# Chapter 27

## The Emperor Has Been
## Naked a Long Time

Examine how some lives have been considered long before the present time. Read the report of distinguished commissioners to Governor Briggs of Massachusetts, dated February 26, 1848. The same questions, same issues, same prejudices as those we have today. Incidence and prevalence, guilt, stigma, blame, dehumanization, God, evil, disease. It was all there then; it is all here with us now. New words: retardation, when once there was only idiocy; etiology, once assumed to be the violation of natural laws. Even the epidemiological estimates then are consistent with recent studies.

Nothing changes; except, today, it does not change differently from the way it hadn't changed before.

Examine the past and see instant replay today. Think of those long gone and gaze at the mirror. Look.

Look at what we revere—competence. Look at what we disdain—freedom. Who can claim that it will be any different in our children's time, or in their children's?

# "Commonwealth of Massachusetts

Boston, Feb. 26, 1848

*To His Excellency,* George N. Briggs,
*Governor of the Commonwealth of Massachusetts:*

Sir:—The undersigned, commissioners appointed by your excellency, under the act of April 11, 1846, "to inquire into the condition of the Idiots of the Commonwealth, to ascertain their number, and whether any thing can be done in their behalf," respectfully

## REPORT

as follows:—

When we accepted the task assigned to us, it was not without a sense of its importance. We did not look upon idiocy as a thing which concerned only the hundred, or thousand unfortunate creatures in this generation who are stunted or blighted by it; for even if means could be found of raising all the idiots now within our borders from their brutishness, and alleviating their suffering, the work would have to be done over again, because the next generation would be burdened with an equal number of them. Such means would only cut off the outward cancer, and leave the vicious sources of it in the system. We regarded idiocy as a disease of society; as an outward sign of an inward malady. It was hard to believe it to be in the order of Providence that the earth should always be cumbered with so many creatures in the human shape, but without the light of human reason. It seemed impious to attribute to the Creator any such glaring imperfection in his handy-work. It appeared to us certain that the existence of so many idiots in every generation, *must* be the consequence of some violation of the *natural laws;*—that where there was so much suffering, there must have been sin. We resolved, therefore, to seek for the *sources* of the evil, as well as to gauge the depth and extent of the misery. It was to be expected that the search would oblige us to witness painful scenes, not only of misfortunes and sufferings, but of deformities and infirmities, the consequences of ignorance, vice, and depravity. The subjects of them, however, were brethren of the human family; the end proposed was not only to relieve their sufferings, and improve their condition; but, if possible, to lessen such evils in coming generations; the task, therefore, was not to be shrunk from, however repulsive and painful was its contemplation.

It is to be confessed, however, that we have been painfully disappointed by the sad reality, for the numbers of beings originally made in God's image, but now sunk in utter brutishness, is fearfully great, even beyond anything that had been anticipated.

The examination of their physical condition forces one into scenes, from the contemplation of which the mind and the senses instinctively revolt.

In searching for the causes of this wretchedness in the condition and habits of the progenitors of the sufferers, there is found a degree of physical deterioration and of mental and moral darkness, which will hardly be credited.

We would fain be spared any relation of what has been witnessed, as well for our own sake, as for the tastes and feelings of others, which must be shocked by the recital of it. It would be pleasanter simply to recommend such measures as would tend to remove the present evils, and prevent their recurrence. But this may not be. Evils cannot be grappled with, and overcome, unless their nature and extent are fully known. Besides, our duty was not only to examine into, but to report upon, the conditions of the idiots in our Commonwealth; and that duty must be done.

During the year 1846, we endeavored, by means of circular letters addressed to the town clerks, and to other persons in every town of the Commonwealth, to ascertain the number, and, as far as could be, the condition of the idiots in their respective neighborhoods.

The answers obtained to most of these inquiries were, in many cases, very vague and unsatisfactory. It was soon seen that little dependence could be placed upon information so obtained, even as to numbers, much less as to the condition and wants of the idiots. We, therefore, visited as many towns as possible, and endeavored, by personal observation and by inquiries, to gather all the information in our power, respecting the numbers and conditions and treatment of the unfortunate objects of our inquiry, both those in the public almshouses and at private charge.

It was not possible, however, to obtain all the desired information, because the researches were begun too late in the season, and because the subject grew in importance and in dreadful interest, the more closely it was examined.

The imperfect results of these inquiries were embodied in a report, made March 15th, 1847, and printed by order of the legislature.

Being directed to continue these labors, the painful inquiry was resumed during the last summer.

By diligent and careful inquiries in nearly one hundred towns in different parts of the state, we have ascertained the existence, and examined the condition, of *five hundred and seventy-four* human beings who are condemned to hopeless idiocy, who are considered and treated as idiots by their neighbors, and left to their own brutishness. They are also idiotic in a legal sense; that is, they are regarded as incapable of entering into contracts, and are irresponsible for their actions, although some of them would not be considered as idiots according to the definition of idiocy by medical writers. There are a few cases where insanity has terminated in total *dementia*. There are others where the sufferers seemed to have had all their faculties in youth, and to have gradually lost them, not by insanity but unknown causes. Excluding such cases, there are four hundred and twenty persons who are to be regarded as truly idiots.

These are found in 77 towns. But all these towns were not thoroughly examined. Take therefore only the 63 towns, in which very minute inquiries were made. These contain an aggregate population of 185,942; among which, were found 361 idiots, exclusive of insane persons. Now if the other parts of the state contain the same proportion of idiots to their whole population, the total number in the Commonwealth is *between twelve and fifteen hundred*!

This is a fearful number, and it may seem to others, as it did at first to us, to be incredible. It is far greater than any calculation based upon previous returns to the legislature by commissions appointed to ascertain the number of lunatics and idiots, or than the number of idiots set down in the pauper abstract, published by the secretary of state, as supported or relieved by the towns. That document makes the number to be only 377; whereas, if our observations are correct, and the other towns in the state furnish a proportionate number of pauper idiots, then the whole number in the state should be over 500. It is probable, however, that the overseers of the poor, in making their return, gave only the number of idiots in almshouses, and overlooked many who receive aid from the towns at their own houses. When a poor woman applies for aid, they do not go to inquire whether any of her children are idiotic or not; whereas we pursued our inquiries into the families, and found many idiots there. However, without any reference to the manner in which other returns have been made, or any question about the degree of care which was observed, by those who made them, to distinguish between idiots and lunatics, it seems certain that our own return is a very near approach to the truth. Indeed, if there be any material error, it must be of omission, for our calculation is not based upon vague reports or answers returned to circulars. We have examined almost every case personally or by an agent on whom dependence could be placed, and in a few only have relied upon other sources of information which seemed unquestionable.

There is yet another mode by which to try the correctness of these conclusions. The returns made to us in 1846, by the town clerks in 119 towns, containing an aggregate population of 213,993 inhabitants, give the names of 394 persons who are considered by them as idiots. If to these are added 361 idiots proper, found in 1847, in 63 other towns, containing an aggregate population of 178,693,—they make a total of 182 towns, and an aggregate of 392,586 inhabitants, among whom are found 755 idiots. In this ratio, the number in the state would be over 1300, even considering the population as no greater than it was in 1840, and supposing that the number in the towns that give imperfect returns, is even as great as in those that were thoroughly examined.

We make our report, therefore, of the number of idiots in the towns examined, with entire confidence that it is not too high; and conclude, moreover, that if the other parts of the Commonwealth furnish an equal number, there are over twelve hundred persons within the State who are considered and treated as idiots. This, it will be observed, is even a greater number than was supposed to exist, when the partial report of last year was made.

The same thing has been experienced, in estimates made of the number of the insane. When attention was first turned to the subject, the number reported was supposed to be altogether an exaggeration; yet every succeeding examination has shown that the number is greater than that given by the preceding ones.

Over four hundred idiots have been minutely inspected by us personally, or by an agent upon whom we can rely. Upon the bodily and mental condition of these will be based our remarks and conclusions.

In an appendix will be found their names,[1] ages, physical condition, and mental and moral character. It may seem to some, who inspect the tables, that they contain many trivial details with regard to the physical condition of the persons named; but it is hard to be too minute in these statements. The whole subject of idiocy is new. Science has not yet thrown her certain light upon its remote, or even its proximate causes. There is little doubt, however, that they are to be found in the CONDITION OF THE BODILY ORGANIZATION. The size and shape of the head, therefore; the proportionate development of its different parts; the condition of the nervous system; the temperament; the

---

[1] We have reported the names, as in duty bound, but would suggest and request that they be not printed, only referred to by numbers. The feelings and wishes of many worthy families would be thereby respected and gratified.

activity of the various functions; the development of the great cavities,—the chest and abdomen; the stature,—the weight,—every peculiarity, in short, that can be noted in a great number of individuals, may be valuable to future observers. We contribute our own observations to the store of facts, out of which science may, by and by, deduce general laws. If any bodily peculiarities, however minute, always accompany peculiar mental conditions, they become important; they are the finger-marks of the Creator, by which we learn to read his works.

There are yet more subtle causes of idiocy existing in the bodily organization, and derived from the action of that mysterious, but inevitable law, by which Nature, outraged in the persons of the parents, exacts her penalty from the persons of their children. We have endeavored to throw some light upon this also; or rather, to give a number of detached luminous points; trusting that more accurate observers will furnish many others, until all the dark surface shall be made bright, and the whole subject become clear.


This is but a small fraction of what was reported by those honorable men. They wrote about the capacities of idiots, their treatments in almshouses and in private families, their problems, their rights. The report reflected concern for unfortunate creatures, charity, responsibility. Without doubt, those good men tried mightily to record accurate observations and make their words represent what they believed. Nothing has changed but the dates and the names. Once upon a time, this report was submitted for the commissioners by Dr. Samuel G. Howe, a great humanitarian of that day. Others have never ceased coming, and society has never ceased ignoring them.

# Chapter 28

## Vanities and Delusions:
## More Questions and Answers

"Professor, the plan requires inmates to risk everything—their lives if necessary—to gain their freedom. It's an appealing proposition, an existential one; and, like all of existentialism, it appeals to the superior mind, not the dull, not the mentally retarded! Never. Ask Kierkegaard."

"David, I don't label what we're talking about as existential. I don't label it anything—but certainly, not that. I could more easily label the plan 'Dadaist.'

"Yet, we are not Dadaists. We do not destroy for the sake of destruction. In the same way, we are not existentialists. We don't really have the stomach to make severe personal sacrifices or convince others to submit themselves to heroic tortures. Essentially, we claim that the inmates—all of us—must rise above those institutions which do wrong. We want freedom for our brothers, both for them and for ourselves. If they are not free, can we be? Certainly, if they are enslaved, what can we say and think of ourselves and our freedom?

"I'm not dealing very well with your comment, David. Partly because I, too, am a very imperfect and conflicted human being, but partly because I don't think our plan attempts to represent any movement or philosophy. So much of that is bullshit anyway. We have developed a straightforward strategy because we think it may work. It has no name or history. If it doesn't work, it will have nothing to do with existentialist or Dadaist philosophy. It will just mean that we were wrong, or we did our stuff wrong, or something went wrong. Look that up in Jaspers and Camus."

"But, it can't work. We're dealing with mentally retarded people, many of them out-and-out idiots. There's no way. No way!"

"You may be right, John. But we have no other way. This is the only way we know."

"Maybe we need faith, not any faith, not a kind of fatalistic faith. Maybe we need a faith in the depth and educability of every human being, even idiots. Maybe we don't understand that concept well enough or have any faith in it because we haven't dealt with our own —my own—retardation, my deficiency, my blindness, my deafness, my imperfect vision, my cold ways, my unforgiving nature, my stupidity. Maybe we can't deal with others' disabilities just because of *our* disabilities, because of our vanities and delusions."

"Don, I understand what you say. But idiots?"

"But who else?"

*10/14/72    Author's Diary*

## "Goo-Goo, Are You My Dada? Or, Writing About Something to Discover It"

Who made Dada? What was Dada? Armory shows, Man Ray, Duchamp's "Nude Descending a Staircase," Gertrude Stein, cummings, Tzara, Picabia, New York, Paris, New Hope State School. All good bastards, rise above your institutions, your craziness, your wars, your evils, your excesses. Ridicule and reduce to rubble what this supposed civilization has created. Your absurdities can cancel theirs. Paris had the cube. New Hope has mental health. We have nothing to lose but this insanity.

We have dreams that regional centers, head starts, better teachers, better something would make life tolerable for the unwanted. But the dreams dissolve because they do not confront the essential problem, a society that can pick and choose who are human and who are subhuman, who are included and who may be excluded. Once, when time was longer and the future appeared to be grander, we had hopes that rational men and women would find a way to make life better for more people. Now we must concede that we have failed, and the only hope remaining rests with the unwanted themselves. They must lead us to a better society for all people. But how? And, if they fail too, then what?

But, also, why? Why might they fail? Professor Gabler said the other day that what's wrong with our society is that we revere life more than personal freedom. That's a reason, and I can add one more: We also revere competence more than either freedom or life. You son-of-a-bitch goddess, Success, you'll guarantee that these poor bastards remain poor bastards. You and your competency-based destruction. A person has the "smarts" or he's not a person. Nothing else really matters or has any relevancy. Only the "smarts" count.

But are those the reasons? Who knows? And who knows on what scene in Act Three the curtain will fall? Who even knows what the play will be about? And the writers and the actors, who knows? And, what will occur between the acts? Just smoke or real fire?

Who can tell a book from its cover, or its title, or its author? Ah, but who can tell a book from its words? If you say most people can, you are wrong, much more wrong than if you say no one can.

How many people on earth know that Horace Mann is a contemporary professor of special education who lives in Buffalo, New York? Or, how many know that brooks and islands have nothing to do with Brook Island State School? Did you know that state schools are not schools? Mental hospitals are not hospitals? Asylums do not provide asylum, attendants do not attend, and physicians do not heal?

How many people would appreciate the inscription on Paré's tomb, "I treated my patients—God cured them"? Who would believe that? And, if one did, what would he believe?

It's like the usual conflict between writer and editor. What does it all mean? That is, who is to interpret art, ideas, feelings? What did Paré mean, really mean, not what he meant to you? Some will say that the meaning and value is only in the mind of the recipient—the reader. But others—writers, for example—may say that the creator's sense of things is all that's important. After the work, it does not matter what others think or how they react. Their reactions are O.K., maybe even good and supportive at times, but that is not something for the writer to figure out. He did what he did for himself; and the reader reads for himself; and people build institutions for themselves, and staff them for themselves; and others try to tear them down for themselves. And each person has his reasons and reasons for his reasons.

Add another complication: What should be evaluated in art and in works designed to benefit the public? In art, the answer is that form is everything, content nothing. It should not matter if you detest the ideas or the politics of a book; the writer should account only for his art. In works designed for the common good—schools, institutions, roads—I think we would be a better culture now had we taken a different approach. We should have invested more in judging the political and moral implications, and the content and function of those works, rather than the intentions of the creators or the aesthetic-objective-insular picture that those works impress upon us. That is, art should be judged apart from the external sociopolitical atmosphere, and public-welfare programs must not be so judged.

Anything else serves people poorly. And, that's what we have, most everything else.

There's an insurrection brewing here. It has to do with the inmates, but only partly with them. I think that those on the outside who support it base their position on two concepts: the right a person has to make decisions about his life, and the potential any person has for learning. I think that the supporters see these as concerns about all people, even themselves. I don't know where I'm going in this, but it now seems right that I tag along. One word at a time, then one sentence, then something to be done. These matters concern me too.

Are you listening, Dada?

# Chapter 29

## Collages

*10/16/72   Author's Diary*

## "Things Heard and More Imagined"

I see your pictures on the screen and I scream and I scream. But only inside. I can't do it. I want to. But I can't let myself join this crowd of professors and children acting grown up, acting tough.

Nice guy, Mr. Edward, hell of a nice guy. But he'll run when things get tough. And who'll be left? These poor bastards and me, Adam Mack, the all-American fall guy.

But it's not just those pictures. Or the poor bastards here. It's me, Adam Mack, inmate. God, can they do it? No way! Dope, don't think about it; don't be a sucker. As the Professor says, *they* can't do it. Only the inmates can. Adam Dope, do you know who he means? You!

Me? You, you, you, *you*! How can I lead—what did he call it?—a revolt? Of idiots, shit-kickers, biters, vomiters, pinheads, mongols, cripples? The blind leading the blind. I'm the smartest, but where? Here! On the outside, I'm a dope!

No, I'm not a dope, not even on the outside. I know I'm not. And some others here aren't dumb. And even the shit-kickers could change. I believe that wild professor. Goddamn it all, I believe him!

And things haven't changed. The goddamned place still smells. Guys are still naked, people still tied, kids still in solitary, food still lousy. And there's still no way out of this zoo, this jail, this asylum that gives no one but the staff asylum—and little of that. What a laugh!

Search, think deeply within the heart; think deeply within your mind. There's a place there, an untapped place, a strength, a reserve to be used by those who find it.

Think back, Adam Mack, to days long past, when you couldn't wait for the sun to shine. Think of Sunday mornings in a warm good bed, with a quilt of down, a smooth cover near your nose, and soft pillows around your head. Think of the sounds of dishes moving in a kitchen below. Your Mom—don't cry!—finally calling, "Adam, Nancy, Dad, hurry hurry. The sun is up. There are things to do, good food to eat, people to see. Aunt Florence and Uncle Joe and the kids will be here in fifteen minutes. There are scrambled eggs to eat, and bacon, and hot rolls, and those sweet rolls you love so much. We'll have a day today that you'll remember forever."

The fair is here. The rides. The smells, the popcorn, the franks, and your hand will be in Dad's. He's strong, and good, and warm.

Adam, you loved them all so very much. Why did it all disappear? Why were you forsaken? Life was good, so sweet. And, now it's gone, and you've forgotten what life could be like.

Remember, Adam. Try to remember. If you remember, you will want to regain what was lost. You will try to recapture the times you were alive. Think. Peel away the years, the troubles, the calluses, the hurts. Return, within the soul, to a time when you were growing, unfolding, when the world was yours, when you had hopes and dreams.

Adam Mack, don't cash in. There is tomorrow for others; why not for you? Resist. Don't forget what was and what might be. Believe in God, and professors, and students, and in yourself. Believe that the world can be good, because it had been good. The evidence is there. You lived it.

Believe so much that you will be able to teach others to believe, even others who never had a dream because they never lived, never since the beginning.

Hurry, quickly, the world waits for you to lead these people to a new environment.

There is nothing new and nothing hopeful about New Hope; but everywhere else, the world can be good. And, it waits for you. Hurry, hurry, there is little time left for people.

# Chapter 30

## Paradoxes

There is a tear
　　But not an eye
　　A leer?
Behind a sigh
Here comes the chow
　　Watch the flies
　　Wow!
You eat you die
Drink a beer
　　Have some fun
　　Cheer?
You must be dumb
File in clowns
　　Leave your cell
　　Grand Rounds!
Then back to hell
Have no fear
　　Say the words
　　Am I that queer?
You're for the birds
You have your woe
　　I have mine
　　You're too slow!
I'm too kind

"Professor, where does Gabler fit into our planning? Where does ideological anarchy fit?"

"There we go again with labels. I think I can deal with Gabler, at least superficially. On the other hand, Gabler is one person who should not be dealt with superficially. Ask your questions."

"I never met Gabler. Yet I feel as if I know him, probably because you speak of him, and he has been here many times. Yet, although I 'know' him, he's a paradox. What does he stand for? What does he represent?"

"Before you try to deal with the tough questions, Professor, remember several of us are new to campus. And, although I've seen Gabler's book, *The Creation of Madness*, would you very briefly tell us a bit about Gabler the man?"

"In a nutshell, Zelman Gabler is an Austrian who came to the United States in the late thirties, completed his medical education here, and eventually became a practicing psychiatrist. Currently, he is a professor of psychiatry at the medical school."

"Those are really the bare bones, but O.K. for the time being. So now that you've dealt with Peter's easy question, Professor, could you get back to Marsha's earlier ones? What does Gabler stand for, and whom does he represent?"

"The answer is 'Gabler,' both times. At least, that is my answer. For his answer, you must ask him. What I'm trying to say is that Gabler is the enemy of metaphors, especially metaphors about him. And when you ask what a man stands for, you require an answer in metaphors."

"Then how can we deal with Marsha's questions?"

"The best way is to sit down with Gabler to discuss matters that are grounded in some reality base. Asking a man like Gabler what he stands for may be the exquisite example of one who has missed the whole point of Gabler's very being."

"Would he visit here?"

"Call him. We meet again on Thursday morning. If he's free, I think he might enjoy speaking with us."

*10/24/72   Author's Diary*

## "Gabler: A Faithful Tape Transcript, Portion of Edward's Class, 10/19"

"Dr. Gabler, you are a psychiatrist; however, you appear to be against psychiatry."

"Not quite accurate. Essentially, there are two psychiatric interventions, completely incompatible: voluntary and involuntary. I have no quarrel with voluntary intervention."

"But suppose a person who needs psychiatric help is incapable of making a voluntary decision to seek treatment?"

"Who is to say who needs what? Who is to stipulate the conditions? Who is to decide what is best for another human being?"

"Isn't psychiatry a science? Isn't there a scholarship that suggests treatments and placements? Just what is the mental health profession—if the professional seems less able to decide about some human being's needs than that human being, no matter how ordinary he may be?"

"The mental health profession is a secular religion, meaning that its purpose is to promote certain human values and oppose other human values."

"Ah, Dr. Gabler, this is where the idea of metaphors comes in. You are claiming that mental illness is no more than that—a metaphor."

"What else can it be? The agnostic might claim that Jesus was not the son of God; he was an illegitimate child. The concept of Jesus is a metaphor. In this same way, mental illness is not an illness; it's a metaphor. And, therefore, the essence of my work is in the demolition of psychiatric mythology. For example, one can label the Jew as a mammal or as one of God's chosen people. The former can be defined in scientific terms and the latter in political terms. The psychiatric industry defines disease politically, not as it has been understood scientifically for thousands of years, a demonstrable abnormality of the body. That is, mental illness cannot be detected on autopsy. No one ever dies from mental illness. One of the greater crimes perpetrated by institutional psychiatry is the smuggling in of values under the guise and endorsement of science. Is there anything in one's genes that causes him to be Jewish or Catholic or Protestant? Obviously, nothing! People are brought up to be Jewish, or whatever. Possibly, people are also brought up to be schizophrenic or psychotic."

"But, Dr. Gabler, there is such a thing as mental illness. There are people who are different from you and me, who are mentally ill, or whatever you might call them."

"Certainly, some people behave differently than other people; in fact, we are always dealing with variability among people; that is a distinction of the human condition that makes us, as a group, unique. However, mental illness is no more than a term that imposes a set of values onto a group of people, quite successfully, because those who force this imposition have large and powerful 'sticks.' But mental illness is not a disease and, consequently, there is nothing to treat."

"Then, how do you justify your existence as a psychiatrist? How, as a trainer of psychiatrists?"

"Because a man thinks, should he be denied an opportunity to live and support his family? Spinoza ground lenses; Gabler trains psychiatrists, and to live a bit more grandly, I talk with people who think I might help them."

"I'm not sure I understand the problem; eventually I may. But, in the meantime, could you illuminate for us how to correct it—whatever it is?"

"Part of the problem is organized medicine in the United States, which is very much like the Roman Church in some cultures, a state monopoly. There has never been a capitalistic medical system in this country. Had there been, the poor would receive better medical care. There would be, literally, free and open opportunities for anyone to practice medicine and for anyone to seek the medical advice he wishes. There would also be responsibility imposed upon those who dispense medical care—for example, both informal and formal sanctions against those who dispense inferior, inappropriate, or negligent care. Anyone can practice 'mathematics,' or 'automobile repair.' The task is to find clients. Licensure imposes the ideology of those with the biggest 'sticks.' To wit, Albert Einstein was not permitted to practice mathematics in Germany, in spite of the probability that he was at the time the greatest living mathematician. Ideologies in Germany imposed severe restrictions against Jews. Were those scientific or humanitarian decisions? In a not dissimilar way, other ideologies impose severe restrictions against the so-called 'mentally ill.' Part of the problem lies in the fact that a professor of medicine at Harvard University may not necessarily be permitted to practice medicine in the state of Florida. He can open a factory in Florida, but may not be allowed to practice his profession if he is not licensed by that state. The American medical system is much more characteristic of the Soviet medical system, except that it has the burden of *both* socialist and capitalist weaknesses—not the strengths of either, but the weaknesses of both. Thus, our medical system must exist constricted by a state monopoly, which limits the numbers of doctors that can be trained, while it must simultaneously exist in a capitalistic system which prevents large segments of our population from purchasing adequate medical care. With our system of medicine, we have the worst of both cultures, with our licensure practices the worst of the worst. Medical licensing should be abolished."

"Practice medicine without licensure? Who would buy that? It sounds irresponsible. I don't think most Americans—doctors and ordinary citizens—would ever support that notion."

"Therefore, if one person claims that two plus two equals eight, and another that two plus two equals six, is it then reasonable for the thoughtful man to conclude that two plus two equals seven? If it isn't, then why must we behave as if compromise is always correct and the majority is collectively more intelligent than any minority?"

"How can I learn more about psychiatry, psychiatry without the metaphors and its bureaucratic institutional weaknesses?"

"If you want to know psychiatry, don't read Freud. Read Mark Twain and Dostoevsky."

"How do you view the diagnostic process?"

"One of two implicit strategies must be chosen. Is it your objective to *understand* why a person did something? Or is it your objective to *explain* why he did something? Most often, we ask the latter question. Hardly ever, even when we want to understand why a person did something, do we ask that person to tell us about his behavior."

"But, Doctor, you claim to want to understand why a person did something. Then, why is it that you feel the concept 'mental illness' is a myth and does not aid in understanding some people's behaviors?"

"Because mental illness itself is a myth! For example, a cadaver can have every disease known to mankind, except mental illness. Searching for signs of mental illness on autopsy is as futile as examining the cadaver to determine his native tongue, or religion, or income. To be sure, there are signs each of us carry to the grave that suggest clues to such puzzles. However, haven't we taken such signs—vis-à-vis mental illness—a bit too seriously?"

"Then, can we ever learn more about the brain and its potential?"

"I'm sure we will. However, psychiatrists know almost nothing about the brain. If anything is ever found relating psychopathology to brain chemistry and structure, biochemists and anatomists will probably discover such links."

"In your most recent book, you stated that there are some people who value freedom more than human life and, therefore, to those people, suicide is an inalienable right. Do you really believe that a person should be permitted to kill himself if that is his wish?"

"I believe that we should try to dissuade an individual from taking his life. However, any person has the ultimate right to kill himself. For at least one fundamental and practical reason, he has this right. Suicide is the one thing that's clearly preventable only by employing the most brutal methods of restraint and abuse. Therefore, suicide is not preventable. You see, there is a distinction between freedom and reverence for life. It's part of the sentimentality so common in our culture that reverence for life is thought to be the higher concept."

"I am now, more than before, beginning to appreciate your remarks, Doctor; mental illness is but another of this civilization's myths and, so you claim, a dangerous one at that."

"Absolutely. The more sophisticated—not necessarily greater—a culture becomes, the crazier are its myths and fictions. A greater society would provide more viable guarantees prohibiting people from foisting their myths on the unwilling and unconvinced. In the fifteenth century, the church perpetrated its myths, its definitions, its strictures, its rules and regulations. Today, institutional psychiatry serves in that role."

"Then, language has a great deal to do with how people are viewed and treated."

"Very astute! In fact, modern wars are fought not for the control of territories but for the control of language. The nation that controls language controls the world."

"Yet, how can incompetent inmates make decisions about their lives?"

"If mental patients were all as incompetent as most doctors claim, it would literally be impossible to run mental hospitals as they are staffed and supported today."

"Then, Dr. Gabler, you believe that many mental patients or state school patients could, in fact, be given a great deal more freedom?"

"That isn't the appropriate question. Ask me if I believe mental patients and state school patients should be given the same freedoms you and I have."

"O.K., I have just asked that question."

"Absolutely. And, therefore, no one should be held in a mental hospital or state school except as a voluntary patient receiving treatment."

"Then, you would support a movement to free the inmates here at New Hope?"

"Support it! I would help to lead it."

# Chapter 31

## First New Man: A Dialogue

"What is Man?"
"One who knows he exists."
"That's Descartes."
"Descartes is Man."

"Can Man endure?"
"First, he must think, so he can be."
"Is that enough?"
"No, to endure, Man must feel."

"How can he improve?"
"He must invent."
"What is his most important invention?"
"Ideas."

"But, Man has so few ideas."
"Because he is violated."
"Then, how should Man meet violence?"
"With other than violence."

"How will I know what I am?"
"When you know what you are not."
"And, then will I know?"
"Yes, if you don't fool yourself."

"How will I know of the cosmos?"
"When you cease the struggle to understand."
"How can I know without understanding?"
"That is the only way to know of the cosmos."

"What must I resist?"
"What everyone else seems to do."
"What, then, would I learn?"
"What no one else knows."

"When everything is gone, what is left?"
"You."
"Then, what do I have?"
"Everything, or nothing."

"But, there is an interconnection."
"Are you asking if a man is alone?"
"No, I'm saying he is not."
"Then, you are wrong."

"A man is not unrelated!"
"But he is unique."
"He is not an island."
"But he is even less a carbon."

"I sense a unfriendliness."
"No, it is independence you feel."
"Whose?"
"Yours, if you seize it."

"What is the essence of life?"
"Inner reality."
"Which is?"
"Hidden truth."

"Then, what is truth?"
"False truth or true truth?"
"THE truth."
"Honest explanation."

"Independence risks everything."
"Dependence nothing, for there is nothing."
"Too many problems."
"And many solutions."

"How do I begin?"
"Analyze things."
"To learn about them?"
"To learn about yourself."

"What should I look for?"
"Your vulnerability."
"Which is?"
"What you will try to overlook."

"How will I know when my path is honest?"

"When you walk alone."
"What is the danger then?"
"That others may follow you."

"Who will our leaders be?"
"Those who have learned to listen."
"Then, how will they lead?"
"By following their people."

"What will it require?"
"Independence."
"The leaders'?"
"And the peoples'."

"Who will follow this kind of leader?"
"Those who will be free not to."
"Who will obey?"
"Those who are independent."

"Then, what is the world?"
"Each person."
"All people together?"
"No, each one counted separately."

"Where is the world going?"
"Look at its past."
"What will we learn from it?"
"That we learn nothing from it."

"Don't we learn from history?"
"Only that we have not learned from history."
"Then, we are doomed to relive it again and again."
"Or, to begin to learn from history."

"How, then, have we planned?"
"Poorly."
"One hears that there is virtue in not planning."
"False virtue, for any road will take you to your goal."

"You are too negative about the past."
"Or too optimistic for the future."
"But you find so little that has been good."
"Because I feel it can become better."

"When will it?"
"When the enslaved are free."
"Why?"
"So I will be free."

"Whom do you mean?"
"Anyone who does not harm, yet remains enchained."

"Possibly for his protection?"
"Possibly merely to enslave him."
"Who are some examples?"
"All those whom we separate without cause."
"Name some."
"All those at New Hope times all those at other New Hopes."
"Define a New Hope."
"A New Hope is . . ."
"Yes?"
"Impossible to define."
"And you would set inmates there free?"
"So we can be free."
"Where will they go?"
"Where we go."
"But they will need help."
"Who doesn't?"
"But you said each man is alone."
"And you said he isn't."
"Then, what is the riddle?"
"First, let's find the answer."
"Which is?"
"Only a free person can be responsible for other free people."
"And the riddle?"
"Why does being free cause one to give up freedom,
"To insure his freedom,
"And enlarge his respect for freedom?"
"Eureka!"
"Those who are enslaved cannot contribute to others."
"And, no one is completely free until all who should be are free."
"That's why leaders must follow their people."
"And the people must be free to choose leaders."
"And, to be free, a man must have self-respect,
"which requires relationships with others,
"That reinforce his freedom and dependence,
"Which again answers the riddle."
"Therefore, you call for a New Man."
"Is there another way?"
"From where will he arise?"
"Obviously, from the ranks of the enslaved."

# Chapter 32

## Adam's Conversion

Adam Mack heard the lectures, heard the discussions, heard the arguments, and saw the slides. And he spent nine hours, six days—Thursdays off—day in and day out in Wallin Hall. Adam learned, vicariously and first hand, about filth, pus, feces, urine, callousness, insensitivity, brutality, and inhumanity. Yet, he also found tenderness and concern amid the human debris. He worked with attendants who did try to deal with overcrowdedness, with tediousness, with the dirt, with the cruelty, with the institution, and all it stands for. There was affection. There was a degree of care. There was a kind of love, not just pity for the inmates. But there was also hard, pervasive, cruelty and equally debilitating unconcern. Adam saw it all and, strangely, watched himself change.

Almost as if he were two persons, one evolving and one observing, Adam took deliberate note of his development and, also strangely, thought it all to be quite marvelous, almost not to be believed—and he would not have believed if it were not happening to him, if he were not able to actually observe it all.

He appeared to speak more fluently, more carefully. He used words—language—that he had not heretofore consciously recognized, much less understood. There was a thoughtfulness about him that caused even an attendant or two to remark, "Adam, you've changed. I don't know how, but you've changed. By the way, how long have you been at New Hope?"

From time to time, Adam had been asked such questions but, so it seemed, they were now very much more frequent. And, he knew,

the questioners were less interested in the length of his institutionalization than in the reason for it. He knew, in the way that people know
such things, that many around him were puzzled about him, puzzled
that he was an inmate at New Hope.

Adam was not puzzled. He was a realist who understood clearly
those circumstances which brought him to New Hope and left him
there. He knew how he differed from most of the inmates, how he
was not only more competent than they but also more competent
than some of the attendants, more competent even than some of the
moms and pops.

Especially now, today, as he observed himself changing, almost
magically, with a growing power and competence, while he knew what
brought him to New Hope, he worried about what circumstances
would permit him to leave. For the first time in many years, he began
to think about the outside and freedom. He thought about the pluses
and the minuses, made careful lists, checked them off, brooded a bit,
and worried.

He worried aloud to a few friends—those who always spoke about
going home. They were safe. It was part of the regular chatter of his
dorm to boast about home and return to one's people. First timidly,
for such talk embarrassed him—because he had no people, no one
to return to; he was alone and would have to make it alone—then
with some confidence, even anger, he talked with some of the fellows
about leaving New Hope. He no longer had a home to return to, but
he was a human being, a man, and he knew he could make it on the
outside if he had a chance.

Adam saw Miss Gossett, his social worker, whom he would visit
when things got bad or when he needed advice. She was a good
person, warm, interested, and not a phony. But she was surprised that
Adam spoke about leaving; for a moment, she appeared hurt. She had
thought he liked it at New Hope, wanted to stay, maybe, eventually,
to live and work on the state school farm. No, he didn't want to do
that. He wanted his release!

"Please, Miss Gossett, help me. Maybe I can be transferred to the
new halfway house in town. I know I could do well on the outside.
Get me a chance. I've been here long enough."

Miss Gossett tried to listen and understand. She was a good social
worker. She was interested in each of her clients. She wanted to help
him. So she promised to look into the matter.

> But don't get your hopes up, Adam,
> You've been here a long, long while.
> Though pretty Miss G. would look into things,

Speed ain't the state school style.
Don't draw your savings, Adam,
Hold on to your "worker boy" badge.
You'll be here tomorrow, big shot.
And, besides, you're getting us mad.
What's the matter, Adam,
Don't you like us any more?
Well, your father was a damned pimp,
And your mother, a dumb whore.

Yet the kinder ones said, "People afraid do not reason well. People who hate do not listen or see. Only love and trust flood out fear, and hate, and thoughtlessness."

But, how could Adam love, when those surrounding him now hated. He felt it, their burning glances, their angers, their puzzlements—all because he wanted to leave, to be free as they were free, if they were free; and now he wondered about that too.

And if one can no longer love, he can no longer trust, at least those who distrust him. With a joke, a wink, a quip, a snarl, a comment, Adam was told that he is no longer Pop's friend, and his friend's friend, and Mom's friend, and their friends' friends, and our friend, and my friend, anybody's friend: "Adam causes trouble. When you need a boy most, he lets you down. Leave, you bastard. We don't care. Leave or stay. You are nothing. You are less than nothing. You don't exist any more."

---

*With his external world crumbling around him, Adam had to survive, had to grow stronger, had to build on his newly acquired strength. In adversity, he grew from within:*

*Secretiveness is the handmaiden of anxiety*
*Anxiety is the enforcer of repression*
*Repression is the progenitor of violence*
*Violence is the catharsis of madness*
*Madness is the escape from reason*
*Reason is the revolt from chaos*
*Chaos is the sperm of control*
*Control is the harbinger of abuse*
*Abuse is the device of totalization*
*Totalization is the process of evil*
*Evil is the flight from humanism*
*Humanism is the hope for mankind*
*Mankind is the center of the being*

*Being is the life of the physical*
*Physical is the shell of the soul*
*Soul is the essence of the humanness*
*Humanness is the universal truth.*

And, from adversity, that inner strength gave him new faith—especially a faith in himself and in his future:

*Knowing is believing*
*But belief is not insurance that one knows*
*And to be certain you do not know*
*While persisting in belief*
*Is faith.*

*Faith may not be knowledge*
*But it is strength*
*It may not be skill*
*But it is method*
*It may not have substance*
*But it is power.*

*Faith is not everything*
*But is there anything without it?*

*There is more to a man than his faith*
*But little to sustain him except for it.*

*And everything to work for because of it.*

*Faith is not the total of a man's needs*
*But it permits him to continue.*

*In the absence of other things, faith will suffice*
*Nothing else alone is enough.*

---

It took some time but, eventually, Adam realized that *he* must plan his destiny; he could not count on Mom or Pop, not the others, not even Miss G. He must design his future. He must think through the options. He must make decisions. He owns himself. If there is God, if there is justice, if there is anything to what anyone hears at Sunday sermons, he must be freed. He will leave this place, one way or another. He does not belong in this asylum. He never did belong here. Probably, nobody belongs here. But that's someone else's problem.

Is it, Adam? No, it was Adam's and, so, he too made a decision.

# Chapter 33

## We Are Our Destiny

The world does not change. Time has no motion. Binet Hall delivers the undertaker, for yesterday was death. Wallin Hall appoints the corpse, for now is death.

> And, somewhere a babe is born,
> And tomorrow will be death.

John Francis Gibbons spoke to Adam. "I am not sure, Adam. It's hard to understand you. Tell us again."

So, again, Adam explained the plan to his friends, to those he chose to trust, to those who were selected as the key people, the leaders of the revolt. And they listened to this leader of leaders.

"First, each here has promised to keep the plan secret from anyone outside of this room until our time to act. Second, each here is assigned a building. We have given you the building that you live in or work in. Next, you are to talk, very carefully and quietly, to each resident who you think will understand and may help when the time comes."

"Explain again what we say."

"Sure, you say it just like we've been practicing here. These are the things you say—easy like, especially at first, 'How are you, Jim? Gee, ain't it a shame more of us don't get discharged? But it's tough as hell to get placed out, huh? We don't belong here. Nobody does, not even the patients in buildings like Tredgold where we work. Well, I know it isn't up to us. But it could be. It should be. Who'll help us if we don't help ourselves? Who is stuck here? And if we don't do something, we'll die here. Do you know some of these places, like

New Hope, they make them change? But it's hard. Even the doctors who want to change these places have trouble. You read the newspapers, Jim. You know what's going on at Brook Island State School. Professor Edward at the University told me—he's mixed up in it some way—that after all the flak, all the TV and newspaper stories, in one whole year they have discharged less than 100 patients, and most of those are just transfers. Professor Edward told me that a bunch of those patients were transferred here.'

"Then, you change the subject, talk about something else until the next time you see Jim. Let him think about things."

"What happens next time?"

"We'll go over that, John, after we get this part set. But, just to get you ready for it, first let me tell you I think the next part will be a lot easier than the first part; and it gets easier the more you do it. Next time, you talk about some resident who you think Jim or Sally, or whoever you are talking to, knows. This could go on for four or five times just like this. Each time you'll pick someone you know is getting the shaft.

"Then, the next part is about Jim himself. Your talks have to get to Jim, and how *he* is getting the shaft. Easy, and bit by bit, but you can get to the guy and show him how he must do something or he'll never get out. And he can't do it only for himself. I learned it and you learned it. Now Jim's got to learn it."

"Then we tell Jim the plan?"

"Right, Mr. Gibbons. You better believe it. That's the time, when we are ready, when we've got a few guys in each building. When we know we are ready, we'll act. Together. With help, though. Professor Edward and those kids he teaches will be with us. They've been working and preparing, getting in shape for this. They've been having meetings with some people here too. And each one they pick, they talk to, just like we talk to the residents. We don't have to worry now about who they are. And we must keep away from the attendants and other workers. If the wrong ones find out, things could get screwed up. Leave those people to the Professor and the students. Just stick to the guys or girls you know who might get in with us."

"Adam, when is the time that we all move?"

"I don't know. Take it easy. One step at a time. There is a lot of work to do, Pete. Let's go over the first part again now. One step at a time. And remember our promise! No one can know the plan until the time to move. Even the ones we pick to join us have got to know only one step at a time so, if we made a mistake with some guy, we could just stop talking about the plan."

"Adam, tell us again about how we are all going to leave this place."

**150**

"O.K., Nick, but first let's practice because, if we don't get this down right, no one will leave any place. We have to do it all. We'll have help, but it is up to us. This is our revolt, and everyone must be part of it or it won't work. We can't count on other people. We are our destiny."

"What does that mean again, Adam?"

"It means that we are human beings who have rights. It means that we have to fight for those rights because other people alone can't fight for us. They can help, but we must do the real work. It means that, if we really *believe* that we should be free citizens, it will happen. If we don't, it will never happen."

"Adam, I'm an old man and not too smart. But I know what you're trying to tell us, and I think the others know too. You are telling us to fight for what's right. And, if everyone here can't get it, no one will. And if we don't fight for it, no one will have it because no one on the outside can fight this one for us. You are trying to teach us that, no matter how we came into this place, there is only one way to get out alive. And it will have to be from this revolt that we get a chance. I promise to work for this plan, Adam, just the way you said it to us. I promise to work with you till the end, no matter what happens. I don't want to die here. I am proud that you asked me to join. I feel good, Adam, like a man. You have my promise, Adam. You'll never be sorry for picking me."

"Thanks, Aaron."

---

To care, to need someone, to give
　He gave, this man Adam Mack
For the public weal
　The common wealth
He not only gave
　He gives
And, will give more
　His skin and blood
But only if need be
　And he gives his soul
And heart
　The pores of his being
To others
　Whatever the cost
Whatever the tally
　Adam Mack gives everything
To that which he believes

---

# Chapter 34

## The Lawyers

"Members of the Bar Association, it is an honor to present my colleague at the university, Professor Mike Edward, who will address us on 'Some Historical and Personal Perspectives.' Mike Edward."

"Thank you very much for your invitation to speak before this distinguished group as you prepare to enter into working deliberations on the law and mental retardation. My comments will be brief because I know you must get on with your work and, frankly, so must I. However, before beginning any formal remarks in reaction to the very provocative papers heard during the past day and a half, I respectfully call to the attention of this eminent group of lawyers and jurists that downstate, at this very moment, the State Supreme Court is hearing the case of *Alice Johnson* v. *The Commonwealth*. Respectfully, I commend this case for your attention. Legally, I suppose, it is a so-called 'right to treatment' suit. But, it also involves human lives that are shunted aside, while others are squandered like play money in some insane institutional game of roulette. It involves abuse so gross that one will find it difficult to believe the evidence before his eyes—the shocking, battered, swollen, and discolored face belonging to Alice Johnson. It involves neglect, enduring and pervasive; yet the state is insensitive to its presence. If you could but read the petitioner's history, as I have, you would note that, upon entrance to the state school a dozen years ago, she was diagnosed as a custodial idiot who required complete supervision. Therefore, the most that was ever planned for her was custody, the most. However, she never actually received proper custody, at least by the evidence of continuous batterings inflicted upon her.

"If you will read the deposition of Dr. William Lee, a witness to general conditions at Brook Island, you will better appreciate, I believe, the source of our frustrations in trying to reform such places. When you have that opportunity, I expect that you will appreciate both the substance of his remarks and their intention, which is to illuminate the belief that there is less inherent in the nature of the mentally retarded to produce handicap than in the ways with which they are dealt. We hope you conclude that it should not be the responsibility of such places as Brook Island or New Hope to determine who can or cannot learn. Their jobs—our jobs!—are to make it come true that a human being will learn, not to decide who should receive 'custodial' care which, at Brook Island, can hardly even be called care.

"This will be the focus of my own testimony in two days before the State Supreme Court. Hopefully, some here will read and reread the material just mentioned, as well as some of the superb papers that were presented during this meeting. There may be a period when we will need your support, when you will be asked to make decisions.

"I am taking more of your time than I had planned. Therefore, I must proceed to my formal statement immediately. This statement I promise, and I promise to keep my promise, will be brief.

"I begin with a simple belief, one that undergirds my work and expectations: segregation by virtue of class—*however one defines class*—is, or should be ruled, unconstitutional. Segregation because of color, sex, nationality, *or* such factors as I.Q., is inherently evil. *Brown v. Board of Education* in 1954 ruled that segregating black schoolchildren is unconstitutional. I contend that segregating *anybody* —the so-called mentally retarded, the elderly, anybody—because of a class placement is equally unjust, if not currently unconstitutional. The burden to prove that an individual requires a segregated environment should be placed on those who would segregate, not vice versa. This, explicitly, will be the issue to determine if mere reform of society will suffice. Or, if not, will even a revolution be sufficient? And, if not, then what?

"Several years ago, when I was less optimistic about the future for people, but possibly more optimistic about people themselves, I wrote that commonwealths must be governed by human beings, not by laws. Our society may be governed with laws for people or, better yet, by people with laws. But, I said at that time, in the ultimate dimension, a civilized community is created by its people, not by its laws.

"Time has passed and, as time has its special way of resolving old issues and creating new ones, a person changes during the process of living and experiencing. And, although I, too, may have changed during the years, I remain unpersuaded that laws are any better, or poorer, than the people who invent, enforce or merely are asked to live by them.

"I wrote then that order and truth are not always compatible bedfellows, that law is not morality in the same way that intelligence is not thoughtfulness. I believed then, and now, that a malaise of our civilization is that truth relates so precariously to justice, and law hardly at all to fulfillment. I concluded that, within the law, too many civil servants settle for the comfort and security of atomistic literalness and find it a prison—not a vehicle to freedom. For at least that reason, insofar as our victimized brothers are concerned—the inmates, the so-called retarded and mentally ill, any people who are denied essential human rights—I said in complete seriousness that I would rather support a cabala than what we now have. Mystical interpretations of our laws at least have the virtue of unpredictability and, hence, there is a chance for good to obtain. A literal understanding of the law usually offers little opportunity to move ahead, to affirm positively. Its seemingly singular ambition is to deny, to reject, to stay within the letter—never interpreting the word and the idea, which essentially are mankind's only special gifts.

"In many ways, I continue to maintain this almost Dadaist streak, the belief that human beings must rise above the institutions they fashion. I continue to have faith in people and their capacity to grow, to change, to shape their environments, to create their destinies, to design futures that will please their children when they study history. Yet, as I walk this narrow line between freedom and anarchy, hope and despair, more and more I comprehend the powerful positive influence that lawyers, if not laws themselves, now exert within our field of work, a field which is no longer easy for me to describe, much less label.

"About a quarter of a century ago—it seems so long a time for so little accomplished—I began a career in teaching the so-called mentally retarded. For seven years, I worked with a group of children in a public school, children who were labeled educable mentally retarded. My class was called the 'Opportunity Room,' and many years passed before I comprehended whose opportunity it really was—mine. During that period, while I regularly taught children, and the subsequent years until the early 1960s, professionals contributed much of the leadership and dictated most of the policies relating to efforts on behalf of the disabled. However, the incredible growth and development of the parent movement modestly shifted, at least for a time, the fulcrum of power; and, although the various professionals and their societies continue to dominate public policy, they probably will never again so completely manage the disabled and their families as they once did.

"In the years that followed, state and national legislative bodies—some enlightened, others dragged or coerced—passed landmark laws to protect, educate, support, and employ the disabled. More professionals were trained, buildings built, funds appropriated, regulations approved, and programs launched on behalf of the disabled than ever before. And, although the cynic might conclude that little was genuinely accomplished through these efforts, more optimistic people believe that the legislative reforms of the sixties led to a new commitment of the American people to reorder its priorities and better serve its citizens with special needs. Certainly, the initial interest of President Kennedy and the subsequent involvement of President Johnson brought great moral and tangible support to what became a popular crusade that captured the attention of many people from diverse spheres of interest and influence.

"Today, many of the gains reported originated in the minds and through the efforts of lawyers, and many of the crucial decisions and policy reforms are products of our courts. Eventually, however, the focus will—must—be displaced again. Eventually, implementation will require consumer involvements to an extent previously unknown, whereby the clients themselves will share in policy decision making. Eventually, professionals must seize opportunities as advocates as well as technicians and scholars, as human beings committed to a mission of restoring and increasing potential, rather than certifying and thus insuring current disabilities.

"As I conclude my statement—more a reminiscence of the past than advice or prophecy—I think of the involvements, the battles fought, the books written, the polemics, the speeches, the exhortations, my inadequate testimony during the Pennsylvania case, and my hope to be of more help two days hence when the Brook Island participants—its actors each as adversaries—convene in court. And, at least today, after reading the brilliant efforts of these distinguished colleagues who contributed to this wholly unique meeting, I feel there is more than hope. There is reason to believe that the world will be better for its people. At least, your work here offers more than a shy faith. I truly believe that the substance of these discussions contains what America was supposed to be about."

# Chapter 35

## Adam's Plea

The boss is crowned.
  The people cry.
Folks in the ground.
  Why?
And the replay?
  That choice again!
Please don't sigh.
  Hold tight the pain.
Ashes to ashes,
  Dust to dust,
What is love?
  What is lust?
Three young bucks sit on a stone,
  Wanna stay alive, wanna grow old.
Wise old men who once sat on that stone,
  Wanna tell 'em freedom's the greater goal.
Three old men wanna tell the world.
  But, who'll pay them heed, not our boys or girls.
Too-old men, too long in the world,
  Had their chance, now they're out to spoil.
The Man is crowned.
  The free are gone.
They're in the ground.
  Within the tombs.

Ashes to ashes,
  Dust to dust,
Living meant it all.
  The "how" was crud.
Three old men back on the stone,
  Two shake heads, the other groans.
Too-old men shut their weary eyes,
  Only have their dreams and a world of no surprise.

Plead with your brothers, Adam, goad them; if that's useless, mock them, fracture them, insult them, plead again, intimidate, yet hearten, plead. Beg, show, promise; break the aimlessness, the rootlessness. Fight the Monolith outside and the faithlessness within. There are converts here, Adam, and you are to be their leader, no one else. Professor Edward thinks well, but he is more the professor than the leader. The others are good and true, but will they defect? Can they be counted on to see it through? There is no one else but you. So lead, or give up the show. Lead, or the others will laugh. You will be safe, because they will laugh at Edward, and his professor friends, and his students. The guys will listen—at least, they'll listen—to you. They may wipe their asses with your words, but they'll wait until you're through; they'll listen.

No innuendos, Adam, no bullshit, no time for modern delusions that make a sow's purse out of a silk ear, no mirrors, no rhetoric, no excuses. Do it or get off the pot. Say you are or say you're not. Lead or sit down. You know, it's either nowheresville or you must announce yourself to the guys. You've played it cozy for a lot of years, no trouble, great worker boy, Adam, ole chum. Now what?

It's one thing to go along, another to step forward and lead, another to know that either you're out front—even as you appear to follow— or it's all over. Mike Edward will get nowhere alone: he is nowhere; there is no chance without you, and without you convincing the others.

"Thank you for coming here tonight. You know me, and you should know that it's not easy for me to talk in front of a lot of people. I don't have education or experience in these things. But I asked you to come here tonight so that I could make you see how important it is for you to join us. Each of you was picked very carefully, because each of you is a person who is honest and strong, and who does not belong in this place. Professor Edward or I have spoken with each one here; we tried to explain why we have to revolt. We have tried to discuss the facts as we understand them. You asked us questions and we have tried to answer them as best we could. We didn't hide the risks, the chance that we could fail, what we could lose if we do fail. You promised to think about it. Now you've got to decide. Yes or no. The time to decide is now; later will be too late.

"I'm one of you. I've been here many years. New Hope has been my home, and the years here haven't been bad. Because of you, I've got friends. Because of you, well, there've been reasons to work, to live.

"But I want to leave. Everyday I get older and, everyday, I ask if the rest of my life will be today again and again. People come and people go, but we remain. The world changes faster than the leaves that turn from green to brown. And, like the leaves, we'll die someday too. Someday, our world will die and we may not have lived during its lifetime.

"I want to live. I want to be somewhere, not just anywhere. I want people to know me because of me, not because the state hired people to know me. There are people here who are paid just to know me. You know, without them being paid to know me, no free person alive might care about me. If the attendants went on strike, you and I would no longer be people, except to each other; and we are not free to be people, only inmates.

"I don't want to be an inmate any more. I want to be free. I want my life to belong to me. I want to live and die as a free man.

"I want to live, to breathe on the outside, to walk the roads and see what I missed, to partly make up for the years I lost. I want to work, to choose a job, to live with free people. There are other things I want that I can't talk about.

"I beg you, for your sake, for my sake, for all the ones here that they step on day after day, join me. We are slaves here. To free ourselves, we must free our brothers. My soul needs to live."

### 11/7/72  Author's Note in Diary

It came to pass that Adam's plea was heeded. The corner had been turned. Each inmate recruited pledged himself to Adam Mack, his leader.

# Chapter 36

## Which Fools – What Sinners?

He might have been my friend,
Because he is the enemy of my enemy.
Yet, he might have been my enemy,
Because he is the enemy of my friend.
Who is he?
He hates everyone,
Because he can love no one.
And he cannot have friends,
Because his venom consumes him.
He is foolish man.

He has great potential,
But little productivity,
Great strength,
But little agility,
Great education,
But little wisdom,
Great passion,
But little compassion,
Great wealth,
For, you are the fool, Fool,
And, they are the sinners.

Upon a time,
Long, long ago,
Or tomorrow,
There lived a man,
Or, so he will,
Whose burden was his sorrow.

For this man found a secret,

That no one else had learned,
And, though they taught it all to him,
For them he couldn't learn.

Whisper, whisper,
Tell me please,
I promise no one else shall know.
Tell me, tell me.
Just tell me,
And, then we'll have it,
All alone.

And then we'll rob the young of youth,
And cut down trees before their time,
And build, and build across the land,
And thus, we'll snuff out All,

Except what's yours and mine.
But little charity,
"Right" biology,
But little morality,
Great valuables,
But little values.
He is sinful man.

Who is the fool?
Who is the sinner?
Who robs man of his birthright?
And, who does mean things in the name of man?

Who hates?
Who causes war?
Who destroys cities?
Who sells its young?
And, who ends a man's days before his turn?

Who plunders for gain?
Who is slothful?
Who pollutes?
Who is greedy?
Who is false?
Who tells tales?
And, who spins intrigue?

Not the fools you call fools,
But your kings and your princes.

All right!
Come close and listen to these lines,
I'll say them just one time.

Each man is his second worst enemy,
And all other men his worst.
Our earth'll be ruled by fools and sinners,
Until there's a reverse.

---

# Chapter 37

## The Process of Unfolding

*11/10/72 to 5/23/73    Author's Diary (edited and revised;*
*I am going to write a story)*

### "On Adam: Notes and Collections"

Inmates' poetry and the poetry about them divide naturally into several types: love poems; hate poems; poems on abominations; poems about human dignity and relationships; poems that describe the natural setting; and poems of the future, of hope, and the hope for change.

And, of the poems that were written about Adam—and there were many —most dealt with change, his unfolding as a human being, his life as a hope to all people, the example of his goodness.

But Adam's evolution had a beginning, long before people took note of it, long before conclusions could be made. Once, Adam was more like most other men—in or out of the institution. Once, he lived his life to escape change, to escape responsibility, to remain anonymous. Once, Adam Mack wanted only to endure today. Once, tomorrow was no more than today repeated.

> Beware, Adam, of your unwillingness to change
> Worry about your reluctance to be involved
> Beware of the depth, the core within you
> That argues for stability
> For permanence
> For a predictable tomorrow
> Be wary of your definitions

Of inmates, who now are subnormal
Of disabilities, that now are handicaps
Ponder retardation that exists beyond the individual
That more than pervades the environment
That more than interacts outside of skin and nerves
That is created by the external culture.

Examine the self-conscious
And, beyond, the subconscious
Your prejudices
Anxieties
The pores of your organismic whole.

Struggle with your resistance to evolve
To remake yourself
To remake the world
As an extension of self.

Pay your dues to your being
Exact every ounce of value demanded
Study each cell
Each particle
For yourself.

Know yourself
To better know those around
And, thus, to create relationships
So that you will learn of you
To comprehend what others can do
And how
And why
As the circle continues
Until the end
If you would plan for something better now
And for tomorrow.

Prepare yourself to change.
It means everything,
So much, that it is everything.
Run to it.

Adam invaded the core within the deepest center of the center of his being. And his own unfoldment provided the evidence that man can change, that intelligence is plastic. As a sample of one—both the subject and the experimenter, the provider and the consumer—he studied the nature-nurture question, and the bottom line of his conclusion rejected the null hypothesis that Adam is unchanged, that he is not today a significantly different human being.

But, as he grew in scope and power, Adam Mack learned about appearances, mirages, P. T. Barnum, P.R., tapestries covering dunghills, the

Music Man—all of these and how they disguise *no change*. He learned
that:

>The more things appear to change, the less occurs
>>There is little that changes for people
>
>The more things appear to change, the less happens
>>For there are few who want to change
>
>Then, why the semblance of change?
>>Why does it appear that New Hope changes?
>>Mental Health?
>>Schools?
>>Society?

>Part of the puzzle lies in the observation
>>That things don't change differently
>>From the ways they haven't changed before
>
>It's a put-on, a rip-off, a game we play
>>Not they, or he, or she, but we
>
>All play the game, and most don't even know it.

>Even Mike plays the game; even Adam
>And there lay the danger at New Hope
>>Not the excesses of the Revolution
>>Not the incompetencies of the inmates
>>Not Adam's limitations

>The danger is the mirage of change
>>The hope
>>The seduction
>>The prayer
>
>The wish that the world will be different
>>If only other people would do something
>
>If only I don't have to do something
>>If only I can remain as I were

>This is what monoliths rely upon
>This is what they fall back on
>This is what has kept them in business
>This is how they plan to deal with Mike
>>With Adam
>>And the others

>Give them the sow's ear
>But scream a bit louder and more persuasively
>That, finally, the state has transformed it

>The sow's ear is now a silk purse
>Believe us, we are your benefactors

>A willingness to believe in hope represents the
>>essential danger
>
>Do Adam, Mike, and the others understand this?
>Only the results can answer that question

And, therefore, Adam learned that, while his experience was unique, each human being has, but must find, that core within, that passion, that thirst to live and grow, that wonderment about oneself and one's unfolding, that key to one's creation.

Change Adam
To show others the way
But, no, not others
Not them
Because there must be a "we"
And not us
Because, then, there must be another "them"
We are them
And they are us
In the ultimate sense, there are only people
And we are everyone

Each person must change
As each is a part of all humanity.

# Chapter 38

## Teachers: On Public Education in Private Places

Through the years, Adam had teachers at New Hope. He liked most of them. But, although they taught, he did not learn very much. No matter how he tried, no matter how hard the teachers appeared to try, he did not learn very much. But, from his schooling, he did learn that teachers know a good deal more about what they teach than about what children learn. Yet he appreciated most of his teachers, enjoyed visiting with them, even to this day. They made him feel good. They were concerned about him, about what he did, about his work and his plans.

During one such visit, Mrs. Jennie Harrington asked questions, many questions, about Adam's current interests. From mere astonishment to incredulity, she listened to what she first suspected were possible early signs of senility. However, the more she listened the greater became her confusion about Adam's mental deterioration and her own mental health. He was speaking about revolt at New Hope! And she not only listened, she not only understood, she not only sympathized, she not only appreciated the logic of it all, she was beginning to think that this might be the only way to reform a terrible systemic malady, of which she was officially a part.

Jennie Harrington, age thirty-seven, married to Slim Harrington, New Hope farm manager, age forty-four, was a teacher, a real teacher. Insofar as Adam was concerned, she was the only teacher in whose class he learned some things. It was in Mrs. Harrington's class that Adam not only learned how to read and write but also learned about teaching itself. Although, he did not—could not then—use these words himself, it was clear to him that the teacher—not the book, not the machine, not the curriculum, not the hardware, not the software, not the procedure—is the method, as the pupil is the objective. He learned from Mrs. Harrington that good teachers are good methods and poor teachers are poor methods, and that Mrs. Harrington was a very good method.

If he could write well, if he could express himself, as some others do, he might have been able to write a book, or a poem, about learning and teaching, and about learners and teachers. The book or the poem would have dealt more with process than with substance, more with interaction than with method, more with creation than with execution. His contribution to education would have described what teachers and learners do, rather than what they are reported to be.

Adam did not write very well and, therefore, he never did communicate those ideas—which was too bad because Mrs. Harrington shared very similar convictions, and she would have appreciated and have been encouraged by what Adam might have said.

But Adam did communicate other ideas to Mrs. Harrington, ideas not directly but entirely related to teaching and learning, ideas about human treatment, educability, the inner development of human beings, Adam's own development, the trap of one-way systems, no-option monoliths.

Mrs. Harrington listened, and questioned, and responded in her typical manner, gently but piercingly. She asked to meet with Mike Edward. She did and, soon after, raised some questions with some of her colleagues, two of whom became interested in what she had to say—almost as interested in that conversation as in the subsequent ones they had with their inner selves, located somewhere between the head and the heart.

These three ladies—Jennie Harrington, Marie Ellis, and Sandy Roth —joined the revolt. Someday, their dedication—not only to these particular events—may be memorialized and sung throughout the land. For now, it may be enough to include in this history their only jointly written effort, created sometime between November 12 and December 11 of the year of the revolt:

"Schools and teachers might contribute more to the process of education. Schools and teachers are civilization's design to institutionalize learning. They succeed to the degree that people learn. They fail to the degree that their influence on learning is—to say the very least—ambiguous. Children learn. Do schools and teachers teach?

"We know more about how children change than we know about how teachers influence change. Yet we know more about what teachers do than we know about how children learn. We know a good deal more about the trappings of education—laws, codes, economics, what is said—than we know about the substance of education—what is done and how. Yet our trappings express nothing but absolute faith in the primacy of the substance and the subordination of the trappings. The importance of our trappings is to deliver the substance, yet our ignorance of the substance causes us to disregard its value.

"Our schools and teachers have pledged their faith to: rote learning, activities to be active, ritualistic devotions, utility. Our schools and teachers have fled from: learning for the sake of learning, have lost desire to learn. Our schools and teachers have fled from the substance of education to the labyrinth and minutiae of its trappings. And, in their thoughtless flight, they transform the trappings to the substance.

"The trappings are now the substance of education."

Eventually those good women learned something more. They learned that individualizing instruction is not sufficient. Good teachers have always tried to accomplish that in their classrooms. But who believes in the individualization of goals? Who believes that the purpose of individualizing instruction is not to achieve a common, or even a stipulated, end but that which makes sense, has meaning for the individual?

Those women appreciated that important distinction.

# Chapter 39

## Clinicians

*We have gathered this day to celebrate:*
  *the creation of a concept,*
  *the realization of dreams long unfulfilled,*
  *the fruits of your labors.*

*We are here to review programs:*
  *for teachers,*
  *for children,*
  *for their families,*
  *for all who seek to help others.*

*We concern ourselves with:*
  *the development of teachers and clinicians*
    *as humanists,*
  *yet as scientists,*
  *and artists.*

*We are devoted to the belief that:*
  *learning is its own reward,*
  *capability—intelligence—is educable,*
*All people can change, can learn!*
*Even the most disabled—even you and I.*

*We have tried to conceptualize:*
  *What is special about special education,*
  *What is inductive and deductive,*
  *What is diagnostic and what is normative teaching,*
  *What is the nature of supervision and help,*
  *What do teachers need, want, get,*
  *What do I need.*

*We have designed a clinic for all people with*
> *special needs,*
> *Especially those most in stress,*
> *Especially the unwanted,*
>> *the unable,*
>> *the difficult,*
>> *the desperate,*
>> *the clinically homeless.*

*We have based it on our belief that:*
> *All human beings are valuable,*
> *And, when that is realized,*
> *Understanding unfolds.*

"We have joined to create an environment where students, faculty, parents, and clients can deal with their assets, their aspirations, their prejudices, and their problems.

"We have deemed this time and this place as an environment for university students who are trained as clinical scientists but, first, as humanists.

"We will engage monoliths, and those who seek to separate brother from brother, and all those people and institutions who will deny a child a chance to grow.

"We will create a setting where victims can be educated, and where those who victimize can learn that the world will be a different place for people.

"All this will be accomplished because we will change, because before each of us seeks to convince his brother to remake this land, he will devote his own energies to that purpose.

"We celebrate this singular day together. And I celebrate you for creating the occassion."

---

"Fine talk, Mike, inspirational. You have a way with words for occasions such as this. I know the chancellor and trustees of the university were pleased."

"Thanks, Karl. It was an honor to be asked to deliver the dedication speech. The Gabrielle Harper Clinic, very impressive—I'm impressed; if the point hasn't been made clearly enough, I'm very impressed."

"Well, I'm a bit startled, Mike. You, impressed? With our clinic, with us? You're such a difficult man to please—don't misunderstand that remark—and you really are impressed! I can see, you are. Why?"

"Because you have created an environment to serve, not to deny. You train university students here to create, not merely to implement.

You are trying to educate children, parents, college students, and—at least as importantly—yourselves. So many of the things I believe in, you and this bunch actually make work. You're damned right I'm impressed. This is the only lively environment for kids and college students on our campus. The rest of the university is an ideational desert —at least, insofar as child development and pedagogy are concerned. To most here, service to people is considered an assault on academic freedom and, as one distinguished colleague in the College of Education said to me recently, 'Why does Karl Viereck bring so many children to that clinic of his on campus? What do children have to do with preparing teachers? They just get in the way.'

"You're damn right I'm impressed. Your bunch is one of the few hopes around here."

"I'm speechless, Mike. I knew you were interested in our thing. On the other hand, I also know you're into the institutional abuse problem so deeply that I thought, possibly, you would not appreciate the time I devote to this clinic. I had thought you were a bit disappointed that I have not become involved with your New Hope State School program. I'm not at all clear what it is about, but I do hear rumors. I hear about lectures and various kinds of meetings. In fact, Mike, I've been hearing a lot of stories lately, some of these kind of nutty."

"Maybe they're not only rumors and not so nutty. Maybe the one flaw with you individual psychologists and educators is that you can't see the forest for the trees. Maybe, although your thing is great, in the last analysis, the test of a person's behavior is with other people in settings more natural than a one-to-one relationship in a 'box,' or even in one of your diagnostic classrooms."

"You know I buy all of what you say, Mike, and you know that our clinic attempts to study the individual as he relates to various groups. I can't agree with you more. The individual psychology model has been our anchor these many years. If that very first rat experiment had included two rats (or three) in the maze—rather than the single rat— the course of psychology, maybe history, might have been significantly different. In essence, we hardly know how people behave in groups because we have yet to seriously study group behavior. Truly, that problem—which is the fundamental psychological-sociological question—is essentially an unstudied one."

"Exactly, Karl! All the things you have said—and do at this clinic— relate so directly to our interests at New Hope. That's why, if I must admit it, I have been disappointed, as you put it. Why—now that you have raised the issue—wouldn't you meet with us to discuss the things which you have heard and are, obviously, very concerned about?

We're old friends, Karl. We respect each other; yet you refuse to even hear what we have to say."

"Mike, you know my temperament and personality. I'm not political. These issues are more political than whatever we're interested in here."

"Bullshit! Sure, there is a degree of politics involved. But I'm not political either. It's just that wherever there is power to be wielded, or money to be made, political questions surface. But my interests are not unrelated to yours. I'm concerned with educability, human potential, treatment, education, development, and public policy as it relates to all of these issues. C'mon, Karl, you just don't want to get dirty. Well, you will have to. You can't sit this one out."

"But what about these rumors?"

"They're more than rumors, if you're referring to some talks we've been having concerning an inmate revolt."

"Incredible. Why? What good would that do? I'm astonished. I wouldn't believe it. I refused to believe it. I even became angry when one of my favorite students—Don Baldwin—tried to explain it all to me. I accused him of spreading malicious gossip about you."

"I know. We had Don try to speak with you. We sent him to you. Karl, we need your help, your active support. Talk with us."

"No. You people are crazy."

"Talk with us. Listen. Let us show you some wards at New Hope."

"No, absolutely not. I will not discuss it."

"Let us show you some slides we have taken recently, a kind of return to purgatory. You'll see that nothing has changed since my first photo essay. Nothing."

"Nothing?"

" "Absolutely nothing, except some situations appear to be more desperate than ever before."

"Really, nothing has changed?"

"Let me show you documentation."

"I can't believe it. There was so much brave talk, so much hope after your book. The President's Committee issued such convincing manifestos. Governors, parent groups, so many slogans—even new money and laws—why?"

"We're not as clear about the 'why' of the past as we are about how to finally move ahead with meaningful change. Talk with us. We need your council and support. Please, Karl. I don't plead. But, if I did, I would this time. Tonight, eight o'clock, my home. Please be there."

"All right, Mike. No promises, understand. But I'll be at your house tonight."

"I think I know how you feel, Karl. In many ways, you are me and I am you. I, too, have dark thoughts, and you, too, have soaring visions."

"I'll see you this evening."

# Chapter 40

## Scientists

"Rational man, what is your opinion concerning genocide?"

"It is too horrible for me to consider, to even have an opinion."

"You had best have one; your friend, Mike Edward, will speak with you again, very soon; and, this time, you know he will come to the point—about genocide, and about you. Then he will speak with you again and again. Have you not thought about mental retardation a good deal during the past few weeks?"

"I am a scientist. I am not concerned with such matters. How can I have an opinion about these things?"

"You are not being honest. You do have an opinion concerning murder, in this case group murder, slow but sure murder."

"Don't be dramatic! There has not been what anyone would actually call 'murder.' Suffering, yes, Mike has convinced me of that. But why do you use such terms as 'murder' and 'genocide'?"

"Permit me to remind you, sir, of events you may have forgotten. During the fall of 1971, a newborn infant was permitted to starve to death, lying unattended in a crib at a world-famous university medical center. Nurses and doctors were ordered not to feed this baby born with a congenital disorder requiring surgery to permit digestion of food. The parents did not allow the surgery, and because the child had what you call 'mongolism,' the hospital did not attempt to override the parents' decision with a court order authorizing surgery. Approximately two weeks later, this human life died after what may have been the cruelest existence ever experienced by a human being— covering one's almost entire lifetime. Was that murder?"

"It was terrible and, I think, stupid of the medical center to join in such an unholy conspiracy. For no other reason than the great harm such decisions create insofar as their effects on medical and nursing students—supposedly being trained to protect and preserve lives—the decision of the medical center was ill-advised. But I'm not sure I'd call them murderers. Besides, this is not an uncommon practice. Many hospitals make such decisions, not only about newborn defectives but also concerning certain elderly and other so-called terminal patients."

"*Exactly, then how can you deny the existence of murder, even genocide, in hospitals and state schools? Do not bury your head in the moral muck, my good doctor.*"

"Possibly, it is in the nature of this thing we call severe mental retardation to expect great disability, and to require extreme measures to reduce continuous and hopeless suffering."

"*Doctor, you know that there is nothing inherent in mental retardation—or any other condition—to produce handicap, that is, to produce a belief in one's incompetency. Further, you know that it is the work of doctors and teachers to heal, to restore, to educate, to protect, to nurture, not to decide who will live and who will die, who will learn and who must fail.*"

"But some do not have the capacity to develop, to learn."

"*Capacity is a function of practice and training. And it was New Hope's task to work toward making that belief come true. Not only should that be their mission but in the ultimate dimension, that is their only mission.*"

"Then why haven't they done more? Why haven't they done these things you speak about as their mission?"

"*Because they—most of us—have a conception of human potential that is more than pessimistic; it both predicts the future and guarantees its occurrence. Doctors, teachers, social workers, scientists are trained as technicians, not creators, because they have been taught by others who have been taught by their teachers that education is what is put into someone's head. To say this another way, one's understanding of mental retardation, and possibilities for amelioration or cure, is intimately connected to one's understanding of his own educability. Can I change? Is my capacity plastic? May I shape my own future? Am I more than a technician, a consumer of medical, or pedagogical, or whatever skills? Or, can I create new learning and living environments?*"

"Then, how I think about mental retardation, genocide, people, murder, institutions, hospitals, terminal cases, old people, mercy killings, back wards, New Hope, science, educability, and myself are somehow all connected. Can I put them together?"

"*You just have, Doctor.*"

174

# "On Language"

The man who claims the kind of objectivity wherein he may evaluate language—prose, verbal or otherwise—irrespective of the writer or the speaker is naive or dangerous or both. The man who makes such claims concerning behavior is a difficult person with whom to deal or reason.

There are few—if any—moral imperatives. There are few behavioral absolutes. All behavior—physical, communicative, contemplative—must be judged, if it must be judged, at the abscissa of its real and related behavioral axes.

If things were any other way, the Sermon on the Mount might have been preached by Judas Iscariot. Or, if that is a poor example, the Gettysburg Address might have been delivered with equal effect by John Wilkes Booth or Jack Smith.

The profoundness of communication rests not with the words but with the language. And language is the substance and reflection of the man, not the shape or sounds of the words.

"Thou shalt not" receives almost infinite kinds of reception from different people and from a single man in varying circumstances. The biblical "shalt not" is not the same language as the "shalt not" of the "walk on the grass" variety—as "I am the Lord" would sound peculiar if uttered by any of us.

---

It was significant that Morton Prescott wrote the following during the early morning hours of November 14th:

> If science is "to know" and treatment is "to do,"
> And science precedes treatment as treatment
>    precedes help,
> Is there an unreasonable discrepancy between
>    science and treatment?
> There appears to be a discrepancy,
> There appears to be more science than treatment.
> And this discrepancy appears to be unreasonable,
> Unreasonable, if science must precede treatment
>    and treatment must precede help.
> How does science relate to treatment,
> And treatment to help?
> Is the knowing of science more critical than the

goal of caring?

Is treating dispassionately more valuable than
   ministering lovingly?

Is man, in truth, dependent on science to help
   other men?

Is man in need of more science or deeper love?

Must man depend on greater technology or
   unshakable commitment?

Will there ever be enough of science alone to
   rescue man?

Might there someday be sufficient love?

Science proceeds at its own rate and in response
   to its own interests,

And much of science is on behalf of treatment.

Treatment is dictated by its own covenants and
   in regard to its own ethics,

And much of treatment is helpful.

And all of help is the objective.

The relationship of science to treatment is neither
   direct nor interdependent,

Nor is the relationship of treatment to help,

Nor is the relationship of knowing to doing,

Nor is the relationship of doing to helping.

Nor should imprecise man expect any different
   order of things in his lifetime.

And, later that week, Morton Prescott, scientist, winner of the
American Physical Society prize for his research in plasma physics,
addressed a gathering at the annual meeting of the American Association for the Advancement of Science. The topic he had originally
planned to present concerned the National Space Administration and
federal budget cuts in space research. However:

Scientists turn eventually to philosophy,
   As theologians turn to Man,
   As men turn to God,
   As those who seek faith bring it,
   As each man returns to the beginning,
   As he turns inward to cope with the universe.
   As he seeks to discover his being,
   As he learns how the self reveals and illuminates.

Professor Prescott began with a mild introduction, claiming that
"our people know more and do less about mental retardation than

any other of the world's nations. We don't have to go to Scandinavia
to learn how to develop better educational and treatment programs.
The Scandinavians, and the English, and the Dutch, and the others
came to the United States and we—*we!*—taught them how, and what,
and when to do what they do so magnificently, to do so well what we
continue to do so poorly. The difference between those Europeans
and us is that they take us seriously, for they have a conception of
human potential that requires them to regard all human beings—all
of the mentally retarded included—with seriousness, and compassion,
and fellowship."

He continued with what will surely read as an even milder reasonable discourse on reform of residential services for the mentally retarded. The text of his brief presentation was tape-recorded and parts
are reproduced below:

A home, a college dormitory, a summer hotel vacation
usually provide normal living environments. Jails, hospitals,
institutions for the retarded and mentally ill usually do not.
The claim here is that they can, and such capability is dependent more on *relative* size and shape than on absolute
size and shape, although the goal is easier to achieve in
smaller rather than larger settings.

As a beginning attempt to operationalize benchmarks of a
normal living environment, one might consider the following:
a. The environment should include—from its residential and
all other *regular* members—approximately three to five
typical for each disabled participant. Therefore, an agency
given responsibility for developing a "normal" environment for 2000 disabled residents would require a very
large—and expensive—physical setting if it elected to concentrate all of its residential life within one central facility.
That is, such a plan would be possible but neither practical nor defensible. Dispersing the 2000 residents to X
number of very small to larger facilities would promote
the inclusion of many more typical participants in the program, would enhance the recruitment of more volunteers,
more part-time employees, more community workers and
their agencies.
b. The environment must be open 24 hours each day, every
day. No resident should be kept involuntarily or denied
temporary or long-term leave of absence.
c. The environment must not compete with existing agencies
for clients, programs, or facilities. It should seek to dis-

cover new or better ways to work in collaboration with those agencies that offer services both to disabled and nondisabled clients.

d. The environment must advocate for a complex, not simple, social milieu, for a vigorous and active life, not an ordered, sterile, and predictable bureaucracy.

The question of residential unit size is not resolvable now, first because life demands too much of an environment to permit the calculation of useful success predictors and, secondly, because we know so little about these matters. Possibly, while we wait for—or strive toward—better data, these benchmarks may be helpful.

Possibly, however, the most certain and, obviously, most facilitating and humane strategy to correct institutional abuses is to plan for the deliberate evacuation of any facility that houses more than ten unrelated and nonconsenting clients.

Who will read the aforementioned and conclude that this was anything other than the mild remarks of a reasonable man, a man of science? All who attended or, at least, most! Men and women were moved, and a few took vows that evening.

There is a universal language. It is composed of frequencies more than decibels, of decibels more than silences, of silences more than articulations, of articulations more than substance, of substance more than words. The universal language is the language of affect, passion, and color. Anyone can comprehend it, as all of us employ it. The universal language pervades all communication, yet it is never taught —because it is always learned before it can be taught.

The universal language is Babel, clarified and made useful.

That evening, Dr. Prescott communicated with his audience. He even clarified important things for himself. That is, his own words illuminated that which he had been previously unclear about and raised other matters which had completely eluded him heretofore.

The result was both his conversion to active participation in the revolt and the eventual enlistment of three colleagues who, collectively, recruited fourteen other participants. Yet, as I reread this paper, it is still difficult—an amazement—to correlate the printed words with their effects, to read the words and account for their consequences, for the incredible fact that rational scientists joined what was, surely to them, a hopeless, helpless revolt.

# Chapter 41

## Attendants

*11/18/72   Author's Diary*

## "Background Notes for Story:
## Personal Items and 'Attendants'"

I am an attendant at New Hope. Sometimes, I am called an aide, sometimes something else, less kind but more colorful. Attendants are shit-shovelers, shit-kickers, shit-takers. We also give shit, a lot of it, to the inmates, at least as much to them as the administration gives to us.

Sometimes an attendant feels so bad about what he sees, or what he does, that he wants to crawl up his own ass and disappear. More than once, I have felt that way.

The head attendant in each building is called the matron. She is the matron or he is the matron. That's the name, don't ask me why; male or female, the head attendant is called the matron.

I have been an attendant at New Hope for two years, nine months, and sixteen days. Attendants here have few demanding responsibilities; there is time to think while on the job, and a good deal of time to write during my days off and when I'm not working. The pay is good, and living in the employees' building saves both money and time. It's a good deal all around, except for the shit I have to take and the shit I'm learning to give. Shit is one of the negatives of this job. But what job doesn't have negatives? And I have time to write.

I want to write better and I work at it every day. It is more than self-discipline, although self-discipline is a piece of the purpose. It is more than being in training—staying in shape as athletes stay in shape—although that's part of it. It is more than being able to, some-day, remember what I was, what I thought, and what contributed to what I am. It is more than therapeutic, although it is my therapy. I write everyday for the same reasons that weavers weave and bakers bake. Without it, there would be something important missing, some-thing I cannot afford to lose.

The first entry in my diary after employment at New Hope noted that:

"One might conclude that an experience had meaning and value if he found it to endure too long yet not long enough, as it caused him to suffer while it helped to create warmth and visions and re-membrances of better times that will yet return."

The following two recent diary entries are familiar themes repeated again and again during the past several months:

*10/28/72   Author's Diary*


## "Observations and Reflections on the Back Ward"

1. There is hardly ever any form or content to patient-staff inter-actions, and *never* any regularity to such interactions.

2. Most ward "workers" avoid rather than work the wards.

3. Patients are "they" or "boys" or "girls" or "material"; rarely are they "Bill" or "Nancy"; never "Mr." or "Mrs."

4. People—patients and staff—are alone for long hours, even during times when many of them are alone together.

5. The institutional plan is always more impressive than its effect.

6. Not only are most of us capable of understanding life in the back ward, we are both certain of its existence and already know a good deal about its essential quality.

7. The unanswered questions deal with whether the back ward is a reflection of the institution or *is* the institution, and whether the back ward is a milestone in the development of the institution or its neces-sary central focus, without which there could be no institution.

# "Benchmarks of Civilization"

*Words are seen, read, reproduced, spoken, mouthed, spelled, and mimicked.*

*Words become language when they are perceived in the context of special relationships.*

*Language must provide both a degree of general understanding and a personal appreciation of the idiosyncratic antecedents related to the language. As language, each word has a history.*

*Words may be no more than noise. Language has particular and peculiar histories that differentiate it from sounds, visions, or movements.*

*As language unfolds, the morphologically similar and lexicographically more or less synonymous often assume enormously different meanings.*

*Consider the following:*

> *overlook—look over*
> *mental—mental retardation*
> *76 I.Q.—74 I.Q.*
> *high, trainable—low, educable*
> *health—mental health*
> *seizure—faint*
> *disadvantaged—poor*
> *teacher—professor*
> *resident—inmate*
> *ward—dormitory*
> *day room—living room*
> *attendant—counselor*
> *parent—cottage parent*
> *care—caring*
> *solitary—solitude*
> *alone—aloneness*
> *human being—professional*

*Language is more than the sum of its words. It is more than a part of life. Language is the expression of living.*

---

Tomorrow, Sunday, is an important day. Mike Edward will be meeting with forty-three New Hope staff, twenty-eight of these being attendants. All have been "tested," are *with* us, at least ideologically, at least we think they are. There must not be a leak. We must keep these people together, answer their questions, soothe their anxieties, encourage them to believe that we have a chance, prepare them for the revolt, and select those from this group who will be given special responsibilities.

Tomorrow is an important day. We can't fail then or everything will have failed, even before we actually begin. Meanwhile, I write, and observe, and write, and ask, and write, and think, and write, and fantasize, and write, and—someday—I hope to put it all together. Whatever happens, the history of the revolt of these idiots should be recorded and preserved for a person to study—more, I think, to comprehend oneself than to understand what has occurred. If it succeeds, its dissemination may illuminate as it preserves our civilization. If it fails, its dissemination may delay our eventual fall. Either way, it is important for me to record as carefully as I can what is occurring now at New Hope State School. That the official—the only—reporter here, one who has been a participant from the beginning, is an attendant amid so many doctors, professors, and other professionals is as lovely as it is ironic.

# Chapter 42

## Walks With a Strong Man

*11/28/72 to 11/30/72   Author's Diary*

## "Conversations and Creations: For Story"

Adam, do you say what you say you say?
Is your heart different from the words conveyed?
Adam, do you think what you think you think?
Or are there gulfs and broken links?
Adam, is your walk yet straight?
Do you hope or pray that they wouldn't wait?
Adam, have you lost your faith?

". . . for my sake. Think about what I've just said, Adam. I'm worried. I've heard rumors. And your name was mentioned. There must be a leak somewhere. I'm really worried. Maybe we should call the Coordinating Committee together for an emergency meeting. At this moment, our plan seems impossible."

"Professor, don't say those words! Nothing is impossible. I remind you what you taught me: we can succeed. You made me see that if we're willing to risk everything, we can accomplish anything. You started this, Professor, and—with or without you—we will see it through."

Stand on a high place, Adam Mack.
Stand with your face to the goal,

And the crowd at your back.

Walk a straight line, Adam Mack.
Walk with that grace and step,
That separate you from the claque.

Think what you must think, Adam Mack.
Think of those who follow their people,
So they may lead the pack.

Tally, Mike
Tally the pluses
Tally all the minuses
Tally all the Tally-Hos

The hunters are winning

And where are the hunted?
Any less tormented?
And the hungry?
Any more full?
And the lonely?
Any less alone?
And Mike?

Where is Mike Edward?
As the saying goes, "Be true to yourself."
Any fewer in institutions?
No, more.
Are they more open?
No, less.

Tally the Tally-Hos, the hunters
The caretakers
The technocrats
The mental healthers
The sophists

And the sick ones.

Remember New Hope is little different today
    So are the others
Except, possibly, they are not as good
    If that is possible
Remember the injustices you have collected
    Is it possible not to?
Except, possibly, for those too numb
    And, there are too many.

Tally, Mike, especially the Tally-Hos, and *remember*, in spite of
your longing for forgetfulness, for numbness. See through the pious

sounds of beaters, secluders, druggers, ridiculers, defilers, sadists, those who would follow orders—those who would do their duty—for the state and department of mental health, right or wrong.

Tally, Mike, and remember that, exactly as occurred six years ago, only *one* superintendent willingly permitted you into his institution to take this recent set of pictures, in spite of the guarantees you gave, in spite of your promise to protect their anonymity and the anonymity of their institutions, in spite of the plain need to continuously share these problems with the general society.

Remember that new superintendent at Newtham State School—what was his name, Oxford?—who reported you to his commissioner of mental health, claiming that you threatened to deal severely with him if he did not permit you to take photographs at Newtham. He sure stood up to you, so the world now thinks. He wasn't going to take pressure from the great Mike Edward, not Jay Oxford! That man is now a hero to many in his department. Who would believe that you were told that Oxford might be worth dealing openly with and, consequently, you asked him for permission to take photographs at Newtham? Who will believe that you never threatened him—how could you? In what way could you? Who will believe that, in fact, he sought you out to tell you that he would help just as soon as his permanent appointment was certified? Who will believe that, within twenty-four hours after your meeting with him, he managed to tell the immediate world that you tried to strong-arm him, but he wasn't afraid of you—no sir, by God. He sure stood up to you, that Mr. Oxford Jelly. You're not so hot, Edward. Ask Mr. Big Oxford.

Remember that only Dr. John Alden paved the way for your recent photographs, just as he was the only superintendent who had the guts and character to collaborate in 1966.

Remember that you promised to remember until all the posy belts are destroyed, all the jackets shredded, all the "time out" rooms leveled, until all of the infinite tortures are forgotten.

Then you, Mike Edward, can begin to forget.

"John Cummings, don't give me that bullshit. Either you are with us or we lose. Either you are with us or the plan is blown. We cannot lose a single man or woman and still succeed. Point by point, you heard the plan, and you agreed to join us. We trusted you, and we still trust you. You must trust us. We will win. We will be free. You will get to that farm downstate. You will get a job as farmhand. You'll save your money and, someday, you'll buy your own farm. You'll have your own spread and a stream loaded with so many trout that you wouldn't really fish, just catch. Someday, you'll have that snug house, and a family, and a reason to work, and to live. Please, don't quit us."

Adam Mack, con man,
Tell 'em good,
For their own good,
And yours,
And mine,
And the world's.

"Adam. Mack. I. want. to. talk. to. you."

"Yes sir, Pop. You sound angry. Did I do something wrong?"

"I don't know. I heard a rumor, a wild crazy rumor. I can't believe it. But I heard from one of the patients that you—You!—are leading a revolt here at New Hope."

"You heard that? Who told you that?"

"One of the middle-grade patients in Tredgold Hall."

"Do you believe it, Pop?"

"If it wasn't told to me by a middle-grade . . . Aw, c'mon Adam. No, I don't believe it. That dumb bastard Louie Berlinsky is getting crazier by the day. Why would you want to lead a revolt here? You never had it so good. Besides, who would you lead, Adam? No offense, mind you. Some of the boys and girls around here—folks such as you— have a lot on the ball. But, let's face it. Who could lead a revolt here? Even Moses would fail."

"I wonder where Louie got such an idea."

"Said he overheard two attendants talking, Schilder from Tredgold and Schmidty, the man in Wallin. You must know Schmidty. You work in Wallin."

"Yes, Pop. I know Mr. Schmidt."

"That Louie sure is nuts, isn't he Adam?"

"Well, I hope you didn't get too angry with him, Pop."

"Naw. To tell you the truth, his story sounded so real that, for a minute, I was tempted to pass it on to Dr. Rabinovitch, just to cover myself. But he might think I'm crazy, so I'll just pretend it was never told to me. How can I get angry with Louie for saying something he never said? Besides, even if I claimed he told me such a story, who would believe me? Then, I would be the crazy one for passing it on. Better I should forget the whole thing. Don't you think so, Adam?"

"I think you should forget the whole thing, Pop."

"Thanks, Adam. You're a good kid."

The air is sweating, Adam Mack. The sky is low and blank. The birds have left to greener pastures, leaving here the sick and weak. And, where are you, Adam Mack? How do you spend your time? Running here, haranguing there, but oh so neat and oh so delicate. Quietly. Quietly.

Harangue, my friend; the time is short. Hurry, hurry, but remember! Not a false move, not a careless word. Show and tell, but not too much. The walls have ears.

Don't scream, even though some ears have walls.

Be a zealot, an idealist, but don't bloody the world.

Win the battle, but save us to enjoy the spoils.

> Win for us,
>     But not on us,
> Or through us.
> We're ready to pay a price.
>     But—after so much—we're hoping,
> The price wouldn't be everything.
> We've been pissed on.
>     Give us a turn to be pissed off.
> That's freedom!
>
> Lead us, Adam.
> You and God are our only hopes.
> Do not forget us.
> Remember us.

# Chapter 43

## Poets

*12/6/72  Author's Diary*

### "On Poets and Inmates: A Story Emphasis"

Many years ago, the people thought it would be good if special homes for mental defectives were created. The doctors believed that such homes would be healthier for eligible patients than the precariousness of community existence. The psychologists believed that such homes would prove more therapeutic than other arrangements. The educators believed that such homes would provide greater developmental opportunities than would public community facilities. The economists believed that such homes would be less expensive. Public safety officials believed that such homes would be more protective of *both* the general society and the defectives themselves. The politicians believed that such homes were what the people wanted. The parents thought that they should be grateful for whatever was allocated to relieve their problems. The defectives, not expected to think, were never asked to comment on the matter.

Only poets—not the doctors, who proved to be wrong, or all the others, who, too, were wrong—saw the world differently. Poets comprehend this life through eyes that see differently, ears that hear differently, minds that think differently, and souls that feel and dream differently. Therefore, poets—neither shackled by the past nor contaminated by the future, not trained as technicians and, therefore, not constricted by that tradition—were the first to accurately describe what had been wrought for the so-called defectives, and they were the first to envision a different world for people.

Eventually, a poet and an inmate sought to persuade people to leave their bondage. It was the inmates—not the doctors—who understood and who dedicated their very lives to this mission. And it was Adam Mack who not only understood but was able to translate a poet's imagery to concerted action—to implementation.

It was also that same inmate who convinced the others that it was both bad form and futile to cavil about past mistakes and even yesterday's indiscretions. There was strong sentiment to drum out Schilder and Schmidty for their loose tongues. Even Mike Edward was infuriated, to the point of demanding their banishment from any further involvement. It required Adam, the inmate, to point out to the others that two ex-revolutionaries would be much more dangerous to security than a couple of loyal, albeit stupid at times, collaborators. Hence, they were to stay, to be supported, but to be reminded to exercise better judgment.

It was an inmate who rejected every argument for reforming the institution, for making it a better place rather than evacuating it. It was Adam who presented the evidence to other inmates, demonstrating to the exclusion of any doubt that, in the past, the "treatment" of mental retardation had been far more devastating than the disease; thus, why should anyone believe that the future plan of the commonwealth offered anything different to these inmates? Adam convinced his collaborators that, unfortunately, whenever the state tries to do something—even with the best of intentions, usually with the best of intentions—there is an enormous screw-up, especially when human services are involved. Case in point: Elizabeth Rheingold, age forty-six, Caucasian, resident of New Hope since 1944. Elizabeth worked the circus freak shows, having been placed by her parents with the Jefferson Brothers Circus when she was fourteen years old. "See Elizabeth, the pin head; see the smallest human head in North America." The commonwealth could not permit the exploitation of an unfortunate microcephalic. Therefore, a suit was presented charging parental neglect and petitioning the court to remand Elizabeth to the New Hope State School for an indeterminate period. Now Elizabeth is an inmate at New Hope and, about six times each year, she is on display at the bimonthly etiological conference where, almost invariably, some doctors or psychologist introduces her as a microcephalic, with one of the smallest heads ever reported in medical journals.

It was an inmate who established the fragile connection between a poet and a group of essentially illiterate revolutionaries, and it was that same inmate who caused those interactions to deepen.

# Chapter 44

## Tradition

Adam trusted people in spite of moms and pops, Binet and Wallin Halls, New Hope, and the seeming hopelessness of it all.

He relied on the kindness of friends,
    and the tolerance of others.
He counted on order in the world,
    and a predictable tomorrow.
He expected fairness from authority,
    and evenhandedness of the law.
He built his future on a sense of order,
    and chose rationality as his style of conduct.
He believed in tradition,
    and, by God, he worked for tradition to believe
    in him.

Then, where was he?
    Conspiracy?
Sedition?
    Insurrection?
Rebellion?
    Revolt?
Yes, by God, yes!
But, not treason:
    to God
    to Man
      or
    to oneself

Adam believed in tradition. But he learned that he was not part of the one he had thought he was a part of; and now he was glad—by God, happy—that he was not part of the tradition of:

segregation
seclusion
hate
cruelty
ridicule
and
alienation

Adam so believed in tradition that he committed himself to create new traditions that would not offend him, traditions that he could love, respect, and count on. He committed himself to values that had truth and warmth and substance, values that had value.

O sun, O sky, O people
    People here, there, everywhere
Happy people
    Holding hands, tears of joy
The smell of air
    The nostrils flare
And, there's a steeple
    The bells ring loud
Another crowd
    Hugger mugger
The world is good

Adam wanted a life that was itself a creation. As with the poet, whose words were meant to live afterward. Adam's life was meant to remain as a model, a hope, that man could be decent, could create from his relationships, could sustain life from the beauty of love, from giving, and from caring.

And now, we lose the sun
    hurry
    hurry
Adam, work's to be done
    worry
And now, it's time to run
    scurry
    scurry
Adam, what you've begun!
Abraham, Isaac, Jacob, Isaiah,
    Adam Mack
Blush not, man for history
    Man for these people
Join the ranks of the remembered
    For we will remember

Isaiah,
   Whom the Lord had annointed
To bring cheer to the humble
   To heal their broken hearts
To announce their freedom to the world
   To comfort those who mourn for humanity
To build from the ashes
   To create anew for people
To repair the desolations of generations
   To welcome all strangers
For we were once strangers in the land of Canaan
Isaiah,
   Step lightly to the side
Welcome your brother, Adam
   Who delivers his people out of bondage
Who removes the shackles
   Who comforts the despondent
Who encourages those who lose hope
   Who cuts the restraining jacket
Who strengthens the weak
   Whose presence glorifies people
Welcome your brother
Isaiah,
   In this time, for all people
In this year of the Lord's good pleasure
   Isaiah, welcome him
Adam Mack,
   Leader of his people

*12/9/72   Author's Diary*

# "And Where Am I in All of This?"

Things are going to happen soon. And where am I? Where do I stand? What do I stand for? In a day, maybe two, it will happen. And I think not about revolt and justice but only about myself and what these fingers around this pen record—or should record. I'm not at all sure I even know what "it" will be.

The problems I'm having in writing about all of this are so numerous as to make the whole deal very discouraging. How does one elaborate on the already known and explain the unexplainable? If the inmates succeed with their wild plan, who will believe it happened the way it happened? Surely, some will say, they were helped by communists, radicals, you name them. If the inmates fail, what will there be to write about?

How I wish there could have been some sex to write about, or art.

Sure, there are some writers who should get their words above their crotches; good things also happen in the head. But hundreds of pages, and thousands of hours of work, devoted to unwanted people who, for the most part, will never be able to read this stuff. Too few people are interested in the subjects I write about, and they—who may have some reason to be curious about stuff that deals with their lives—can't read very well, if at all. A great selling combination that the publishers will give anything to avoid.

Well, maybe, although it's not art I write about, it's art I write *for.* During these two—almost three—years, I've learned that, while art can't be my religion, it can be a passion. Maybe, even while it can't really be a love, it may explain love—even more, expand it. Hooray, I write for art; better keep that one to myself for awhile.

But if I really do something good with this stuff—I can say "if," can't I?—I'll show how some people are victims of their environment. But this crowd of inmates is different; they're victims of the ages. If my stuff is good, it will show the difference between local mistreatment and systemic-generic-legal-sanctioned-intergenerational abuse.

There is one thing I am certain about. I'm with the inmates to the end. I don't see how we'll get them out, free, but I'm with them, win or—more likely—lose!

How can we win? I'll settle for a tie. But what's that? What, some smart-ass will ask, does winning mean? Maybe winning is losing? Whatever, I'm with the inmates to the end.

*12/10/72   Author's Diary*

# "While I Wait"

1. If the work is honest, it will lead to the writer. It's O.K. not to set it down on paper; but if one does, one should not persecute truth because he has become uncomfortable with the responsibility.

2. I must include everyone who should be a part of the story.

3. It hardly matters what the writer intends to say, or seems to, say; that is, it hardly matters to anyone but the writer—and with some writers, that's everything.

4. One observation I can make from all of this is that people have almost infinite ways to disavow themselves of all responsibilities for their actions. And they have their reasons. No longer does one person plan and implement evil. One plans, another prepares the setting, another executes, someone else evaluates, and no one is responsible. This may be a key factor for the increase of isolation, segregation, and abuse in our society. The fragmentation of the evil flourishes unimpeded because no one is responsible for it.

5. To write with passion is to always risk everything and usually gain nothing; yet, for some, to write at all is to write with passion.

6. The truth in literature lies not in facts or in accuracy but in how the whole of the work permits one to see the truth. The words, themselves, are as nothing. This is why mere facts do not make great books; wisdom is needed.

7. The artist—not always the "best" writer—writes what he wants to write; the hack writes whatever he is paid to write. It's O.K. to receive money because you've written a book. But it's not the same thing if you write what people pay you to write. Yet, I think it is hard, even for the honest man, to know why, or for whom, he is writing.

8. Behavioral scientists and doctors may protect or prolong your life, but they can't make it worth living.

9. I feel that, today, the only freedom left is what's in the mind, and that hangs by a spider's thread.

10. Writing must be judged on its style and substance; not either, but both. There isn't one without the other, for style molds substance and, out of the matter of writing, form is created. And what holds it all together? Sincerity. On the other hand, one should not confuse an elegant prose style with quaintness or inadequate vigor. One should not, but today, who doesn't?

11. One reason I write is to think through my life. What could be more important to me?

12. It is as difficult to know good from brilliant writing as common sense from wisdom. Genius is always unique and, thus, difficult to recognize. But so is anything unique, for example, craziness. Hence, there is confusion here. For example, the first problem with anything avant-garde is that few will know—and yet fewer would know who those few are—what is garbage and what is vanguard, what is Babel and what is Bloom, what is cant and what is canto.

13. Breeding serves the writer; overbreeding dooms him.

14. The writer is as lucky to have a good reader as the reader a good writer.

15. The burden of the critic is that, unlike the Lord, he is never sure that his judgment is accurate or that his reasoning is adequate. Another, that he can only deal with someone else's work, not his own—for that job is reserved for the critic of critics, the high muck-a-muck in the academy. And who critiques him? Obviously, none else but God alone.

16. More on critics: they don't teach the writer, only—and only sometimes—the reader. That's what writers should think about. Writers must do what they have to do, not heedlessly but uncompromisingly, even poor writers, even poor critics who, too, are writers of sorts. Writers must forget their critics. They must think only of what they must write, which is to describe what they see and feel.

17. If only we would understand that there are no perfect books but many precious reviewers. For example, is it so defenseless for a writer to admit that he no longer remembers what he meant by that line, or phrase, or verse? Isn't it enough that it once had meaning for him and, in spite of his feelings now, it may still have meaning for the next reader?

194

18. And, what about writers: they must contend with three human traits—self-justification, embarrassment, and a sense of privacy. To write, one must try to rise above those traits, alone. For, although the writer seeks to share his work, he writes alone and lives in a private world. His is a confusing role and, thus, a difficult life.

19. The best a writer can do to recreate the past is to work at the reconstruction of certain specimens of a given life or of a group's activities. True and vivid specimens are more central to an adequate restructuring of the past—that is, to biography and history—than representativeness of evidence.

20. Wisdom leads to wisdom. And so the trick is always in how to begin things. Start. Plunge. Take a risk. Begin by beginning. Write by writing. Oh, if I were but as wise and as sure as I appear to myself at this moment. . . .

*12/11/72   Author's Diary*

# "To Hurry the Moment; to Think While Not Thinking About What Will Be"

1. Readers, too, influence books, by words from their mouths. Most good books are read—in spite of critics; and most poor ones are dismissed eventually, irrespective of what critics write or the craziness of the times. The people know what words are for. And they, collectively, best know what's in our culture. Good is good.

2. People who write books should consider the possibility that the very beginner and the advanced scholar are the most difficult to write for—and to. They are the most critical, most in need of help, and most neglected.

3. Honesty can be a nuisance, or a way of life.

4. Being a good hack writer is akin to the title of shortest giant in town.

5. As sounds interrupt silence, thoughts intrude into one's world of thoughtlessness.

6. A reviewer may be honest yet misrepresent the writer; in the same manner, he can be dishonest while representing him. This is why, despite my romanticism about honesty in literature, I also believe that it is not impossible for a dishonest writer to create a work that reflects the real life.

7. It may be good for some writers to do other work, such as to teach school or attend inmates. It helps to discourage them from writing too much or too quickly.

8. The writer doesn't need critics or journalists to judge him or his work. He can do that sort of thing himself. But I think it's a difficult job, and most writers do it poorly, if at all—as do most critics.

9. When I am told that a book is full of wit and charm, I usually find that it is also full of something else.

10. I think I often write about something to find out if I understand it or could support it.

11. When there is general ignorance or misunderstanding about a problem, science certifies a lie as smoothly as a truth. Some may contend that it wasn't science that authenticated the myths concerning homunculus and alchemy. Maybe, but then it wasn't religion that prompted the blood baths of the Crusades; and it isn't the tarot card that's the fake, only the card-carrying cad, a faker dressed in fakir's clothing.

12. The academic tradition is to mistrust the abstract, the broad, the facile, the light, the collage. And, in art, those are the ingredients of most things found to be worthwhile. Possibly that's why scholarship and art have not existed gracefully together.

13. Those who spend their lives "selling" ideologies should be known for what they are, salesmen. And, would you trust a salesman, even if he were a scholar or a scientist? Even when he's right, he's more interested in his ideas and his benefit than in yours. Should you, then, be uncritical of his ideas, his objectivity, his interest in the common good, his truth?

14. Everything is here for the writer to pluck, if he could. The world has everything he needs. It's all around him. That's where the ideas are, the connections, the history. Everything is outside of him, the stuff the world is made of. He need only take what he should and put it together the right way. That's all.

15. Institutions are the "best" places to study severe handicapping conditions; open settings, the most difficult and misleading. Why? Essentially, severe handicaps occur very infrequently. Therefore, their rarity in ordinary environments often causes even a sophisticated observer to ascribe certain traits and characteristics to a person's handicapping condition, rather than to the person. That is, when there is no, or little, base for comparison or frame of reference, each case is the syndrome model. On the other hand, when one observes many so-called mongoloids, etc., etc., etc., it becomes clearer that as much variance exists among the handicapped as the nonhandicapped—maybe more; each condition is a mix of individual-specific and disease-specific influences, and only the observations of many people help one to understand that simple, often unappreciated, fact. Institutions provide the concentrated population to permit an adequate study of variance. Unfortunately, they also exemplify the absolutely poorest ways to deal with human beings.

# Chapter 45

## With Thee Will I
## Destroy Kingdoms

At 11:55 A.M., on December 11, 1972, every resident of New Hope State School—sustaining each other, aided by thirty-six university students, nine college professors, twenty-one local citizens, and forty-three New Hope staff—stopped what he was doing to now engage who and whatever caused him to remain an inmate. By specific count, this force included:

2332 inmates
   21 undergraduate students
   15 graduate students
    1 professor of special education
    1 professor of psychiatry
    2 professors of psychology
    3 professors of physics
    2 professors of mathematics
   13 so-called housewives
    2 community physicians
    1 attorney
    1 grocer
    1 retired policeman
    1 automobile mechanic
    1 farmer
   28 New Hope State School attendants
    1 New Hope State School pediatrician

1 New Hope State School psychologist
1 New Hope State School dentist
1 New Hope State School pharmacist
3 New Hope State School teachers
2 New Hope State School nurses
1 New Hope State School farm foreman
3 New Hope State School social workers
2 New Hope State School maintenance men
_____
2440 Total

Each person took an assignment—to sit as quietly as he could, or to hold a child on his lap, or to comfort a frightened elderly man, or to sing a song from time to time, or to hold someone's hand, or to whisper encouragement to one who needs it, or to try and explain things again to one who wishes it, or to just be there with your brothers and sisters—each one to remain steadfast.

The world stood still. An almost—not almost!—miraculous calm enveloped buildings that had never known anything but the din and shuffle of screaming heads on aimless trunks and legs.

Minutes passed. Then some staff confusion. Soon it spread to the Administration Building; greater confusion. Tell the doctors.

"Got some trouble in Binet, Doctor."

"What kind of trouble?"

"The patients just sat down, and there are other people with them, also sitting."

"What do you mean, 'sat down'?"

"They just sat down, with the others."

"What others?"

"I don't know. But Schmidty is with them."

"Who's Smitty?"

"No, not Smitty, Schmidty, one of the attendants. He sat down with them, too, on the floor. I asked them to get up and go back to their dorms, but they just looked at me and smiled. Schmidty, you know him. He just transferred to Binet."

"Ridiculous. Tell them to stop this nonsense. Tell them I say they must stop this at once."

"But this is happening in every building, even in those on the hill. It's happening in the back wards, even in Wallin."

"That's ridiculous."

"Doctor, please see for yourself."

> The doctor saw for himself
> All the doctors saw for themselves
> But none saw what needed to be seen

No one saw anyone but himself
No one saw power growing
No one saw courage rising
No one saw a people moving
No one saw resolve unfolding
Except those who looked beyond themselves
Except those who felt that each is a part of a whole
Except those who knew that groups are not sums
    of parts
Except those who sought to understand

The one who really understood saw love and courage, which brought him strength to change.

Hours passed. Doctor, Doctor, what do we do? Doctor, Doctor, give us some clues. Doctor, Doctor, settle this, whatever it is.

How?
How?
How?
But,
Why?

Why do you do this to us, my children?
We are not your children!
But, am I not your caretaker?
You never cared for me.
You will obey us.
I deny your authority.
We will punish you.
You have, many times before.
I have the power.
We have taken it away.
Don't make me laugh.
Rather you should despair, for what you had wrought.

Twenty-four hours! Incredible. Television, radio, newspapers, Governor Majors, the Commissioner of Mental Health, everyone, are all saying something, pleading, screaming, arguing, crying; please, please, please—go back to your dorms.

"Ladies and gentlemen, as your governor, I promise you that no harm will come to these unfortunate patients and the misguided outsiders who put them up to this. But they must stop. It will get them nowhere, merely set our programs back, make us and our leaders appear foolish, a blot on the state. Let them be reasonable. Let's not impair the goodwill that was created during all these years of solid community support for mental health. Why, in the next fiscal budget alone, there will be more resources than ever before to alleviate institutional overcrowdedness and to develop programs to deal with our problems. . . ."

"We are in a state of crisis. A few radicals have taken over New Hope and, to deal with them, we might injure defenseless patients. . . ."

"You have just heard Superintendent Lenz of the New Hope State School; Clay Burton, WNHC Total News."

"Ladies and gentlemen, as President of the State Association for Retarded Children I can sympathize with the motives of this group of outsiders who are trying to achieve what so many of us have worked for these many years. But, I must condemn, in the strongest terms possible, both their tactics and ruthless disregard for the welfare of our retarded residents. This strike may set the movement back fifty years. . . ."

"What I am observing here at New Hope is unbelievable. Retarded patients completely paralyzing an institution. They haven't eaten or left this day room in Wallin Hall—and in the other buildings—for two days. And they appear determined to sit here until their demand is met—which they will tell only to the governor and State Commissioner of Mental Health. This is Dan Jackson, Channel 9, Eyewitness News.

"Kathy, good for them."

"Good for whom, Calvin?"

"Good for those inmates. I know that place. I've delivered parcels from the store to New Hope for twenty to twenty-five years. Good for them."

"Calvin Hightower, what are you talking about? What do you mean, 'Good for them'?"

"I mean that I'm glad they're on strike. Some of them are treated like animals, and most of the others never belonged there in the first place. Good for them. Damn it, those bastards who run that place should be jailed for some of the things I've seen them pull."

"Calvin! I've never heard you so angry. We've been living almost in the shadow of New Hope State School since we were married, and I don't think we ever had a serious conversation about the institution."

"Doesn't that tell you something?"

# Chapter 46

## Points of Contact

(1)

"Dr. Bernard, may I speak with you for a moment?"

"Please, very softly; Joseph has just fallen asleep. He has no experience to help him deal with changes in his daily routines. He's frightened now, hasn't slept well at all. Joseph is such a delicate child, very frail, and he's been so isolated here, removed from an active life. He needs sleep; please, softly."

"Yes, I understand, Doctor; I'll whisper. The Coordinating Committee is meeting now; they've been told that you are unable to leave Joseph at this time. However, your counsel is requested. There are decisions to be made in response to an offer we've just received from Governor Majors."

"What do you mean, 'offer'? We make no bargains. The committee has made its decision. We must adhere to our plan, our decision. Why should we be concerned with the governor's offer, or what he says, or what he advises? We should not be very interested in their thinking, but in ours. Haven't we agreed that it's too late—if ever there was a time—for anybody but the inmates to make offers? And, I'm sure you remember what the inmates' demand to the governor will be."

"Shouldn't we discuss the matter?"

"Haven't we just done that?"

"No, I mean with the Coordinating Committee."

"Please tell them that, for two reasons, I believe such a discussion would be a decided error. First, we have discussed all the pros and cons of various strategies and tactics. Our decision was achieved after many, many hours of presentations, debates, and eventual consensus. Our plan is based not only on whatever evidence and thinking we were able to muster but also on its overall agreement with the philosophical underpinnings of the revolt. To now renegotiate our general strategy is to court dissension, confusion, and doubt among our cohorts. Considering his offer is exactly what Sam Majors wants us to do. Obviously, we should so arrange events that he does what we want, rather than vice versa."

"And the second reason? You said there are two reasons why it would be erroneous to attempt to redraft our global plan or to develop some compromise with the commonwealth."

"Joseph; he's the second reason. I have little time for fruitless—in this case, dangerous—meetings. In the past, so much of my efforts involved policy matters, what was best for the group, the larger society. My role today is less the policy maker and more the provider, the helper. Number one, I thought—and think—we had agreed on a firm policy. Adam Mack and other inmates—not I—represent the major interests here and, therefore, they must give their time to think through whatever questions crop up. Number two, I am responsible to Joseph. I belong with him, especially now while he's attempting to adjust to this new environment.

"To be explicit, to better answer your original request, I will attend a Coordinating Committee meeting only if it is to deal with a plain emergency or when the governor comes here to receive our demand. Further, I will be able to attend such meetings only when Joseph is feeling more comfortable and if an appropriate noncommittee member can be enlisted to relieve me. I too, have responsibilities. I am needed here, with Joseph."

(2)

"Prescott, if you believe those gangsters, you're denying history; you are foolish. Excuse me, please; I'm upset."

"Zelman, I don't necessarily believe them. But, shouldn't we, at least, listen to their offer?"

"No! Cy Bernard is right, 100 percent! What offer? First, I see no offer, only the offer of a possible offer. Second, we have agreed on a demand; what is this nonsense about an offer? We will demand, as planned, directly to Majors. Nothing else will suffice, and the demand must be honored 100 percent—100 percent—or we continue this course, at least until the inmates order us to withdraw or compromise. The decision, any strategic decision at this point, is completely the inmates' responsibility."

"Dr. Gabler is correct."

"Thank you, Adam."

"But, Adam, how can you make that judgment so quickly?"

"We had made it—all of us—during several weeks of labored discussions, not quickly at all. You, Dr. Prescott, seem to want to tempt us to quickly revoke what had been planned so carefully. Besides, while you ladies and gentlemen have been arguing about the governor's message to us, I asked the residents on the committee to meet so that we might review matters. They have asked me to report that their position is firm; we proceed exactly as planned."

(3)

Karl Viereck sat quietly, thinking. It was 11 P.M. and the day room was still. It was easy to be here, not actually alone but within himself. He thought of himself as comfortable in almost any setting, even this unusual place. For, if he were a boastful man, he would admit that very little involving human beings was completely strange to him, possibly because all of human affairs was so compelling, so intriguing.

He thought about these past hours and what they had meant to him. Assigned here, a dormitory for elderly men, he was able to envision his future—and to remember the past. How very different from his father (may he rest in peace) were these gaunt old men. Yet, how much alike they were, especially at the end. We all return to the ground and, at the end, we all seek comfort, and warmth, and someone to hold a hand to reduce the terror in our puzzled, hurt eyes. That was his father and these men here and, if he lives enough years, that will be Karl Viereck. So, he holds that worn hand, and gently rubs a tired back, and learns and learns about Karl Viereck.

(4)

Jennie Harrington had few moments to stop, much less to think about things. There was work to be done, active work, stuff that teachers are used to—are trained for or are born for—and stuff that children expect from teachers, even the children of New Hope. And through it all—the hours that lengthened to days—Jennie, and Marie Ellis, and Sandy Roth, and those who worked with them, made the time count for the children; it was said later that the kids were the easiest to manage and appeared to respond to the events most naturally. It was also said that Jennie and the others with her were inexhaustible, warm, firm, loving, ingenious, super people who communicated the needs of the revolt to the littlest participants. Some said that this, truly, was the miracle of the revolt of the inmates.

And those who heard that remark could not disagree.

# Chapter 47

## Two Bowlers

"Hi, Carol, where are you rushing? And why didn't I see you at bowling league at one o'clock? Why was it canceled? I was the only one who showed."

"In a hurry, Velma; got to get to the junior high, make some coffee."

"Having a meeting? What about the bowling cancellation?"

"Don't kid me; surely you know about it. Everyone knows."

"Know about what? And I'm not kidding."

"The state school revolt."

"What should I know? Certainly I know about the revolt. Everyone in America knows about that. But what should I know, specifically, that everyone else seems to know?"

"The meeting at 3:00 P.M. in the junior high. That's why I have to rush. I'm responsible for the coffee."

"What meeting!"

"Town meeting. It was in the newspaper, on the TV and radio; we had a telephone crew calling names in the phone book. Where have you been?"

"Oh! No wonder a lot of the shopkeepers put early closing signs on their doors and windows today. I've been downstate, visiting my mother for a couple of days. I had told you she was ill. Got back about 12:45, called Jim at the office; he had already left for lunch, so I went to the alley. No one was there."

"Certainly. Everyone in town will be at the meeting. We just couldn't get in three games and make the meeting, so we decided to reschedule today's games."

"Please, fill me in. Why the meeting?"

"O.K., but I've just got to run. People here want to talk about what we should have done all these years. Did you see those pictures on television? Now, some of the stories are finally coming out."

"You want to talk about what we should have done! What good is that now?"

"No, you don't understand. As Pete Langer said this noon, we want only to discuss what's happened in terms of what we have to do now. Most of us seem to have made up our minds that, whatever happens during the next few days, we're going to support these inmates. We want to be prepared to help them change that institution or achieve whatever goals they're working for—and the rumors are wild, but most of us don't take those too seriously."

"Then, how will you decide what we can, or should, do if all we have are rumors?"

"Well, that's why we are meeting. Ken Winkleman, Pete, and a couple of the Town Council members spent last evening and most of this morning with the inmates at New Hope. I was told that they learned a good deal about the revolt that wasn't in the newspapers or on TV. I was also told that they are very impressed with the leader of the revolt."

"That professor, people have been talking about him; Edward, isn't it?"

"No, not the professor. The leader of the revolt. He's an inmate. Someone said his name is Adam Mack. Ken and the others will report what the inmates want and how they hope to achieve their goals.

"Really, I've got to rush."

"I'll come along and help. You sound as if you can use all the help you can get."

"Sure can. But you better save your real support for the inmates."

"I guess you're right."

# Chapter 48

## Things Sam and Chuck
## Might Better Have Known

"I refuse to be intimidated. I refuse to meet with a rabble of Bolsheviks and idiots. The dignity of my office wouldn't permit it."

"Governor Majors, if I can respectfully disagree. The security of your office may not permit any alternative. Can you afford a violent uprising? Shouldn't you go to the people in times such as these? Think of yourself as a humble man, a concerned man, a humanitarian who wants to alleviate suffering. Can you afford to be known as a man who would kick a handicapped person while he is down? Remember, we are also looking toward '76, and what the whole nation thinks about us will be very important."

"Get Commissioner Wiley on the line."

> Smart man, Sam
> Got to giv'ya a hand
> Best gov in the land
> Makes pretty castles in the sand

It was an open secret around the State House that Sam Majors had little regard for Charles Wiley. He used to tell his aides that the dumb bastard Wiley needed mental health services more than the patients. The governor kept him in office as sort of a private joke, deserved by those stupid, pedantic psychiatrists running the institutions. Lately, the joke was getting more public and less funny.

O.K. Chuck

Wanna wish you luck
Remember not to cluck
When you lie to those schmucks
Sam and Chuck went to the school
To speak with hips and utter fools
Sam came back quite contrite
And poor old Chuck is still in fright
It's simple
It's neat
All we ask
Is to leave

All they asked was to leave. Then, they said that they're asking only because that's the polite idiom for demanding. Then, they said that they don't care what the governor wants. They don't give a shit how the commissioner feels. The Association for Retarded Children is fine, and they have been grateful for their help, but they ought to mind their own business this time—and would you please tell that to Mom and Dad too! Then, they said that there is only one way to end this revolt, and that one way is to let the inmates leave. Then, they said that where they go, what they do, how they'll live is their business. Then they said that every inmate must be included, every inmate! Then, to emphasize the point, they said that even bed patients and sick patients were to be included. Then, they excused the governor and the commissioner, told them to go away and come back only when they were ready to unlock the doors and permit everyone—everyone—to walk out of that hell. Then, one of them quoted something from the Bible, which was difficult to understand, but seemed to imply that God was on their side and, if the Monolith resists, these inmates will destroy it.

Sam and Chuck left quickly.

*12/13/72   Author's Diary*


## "Postscript on Things Sam and Chuck Might Better Have Known"

Had these representatives of the people known a few basics about this revolt, they might have joined it or—more likely—they would have been able to squash it.

Did they know that Adam Mack was the leader of this group—in every sense?

Did they know that persistent abuse may make the weak strong and the cowardly heroic?

Did they know that most people have an essential goodness that constantly seeks expression?

Did they know that their Department of Mental Health gives corruption a bad name?

Did they know that, for people who yet have life, a few days of freedom is better than their allotted years as inmates?

Did they know that, to those people, anarchy represents greater hope than what they found in the bureaucracy?

Did they know that Adam Mack would resist them to the end beyond the end, and that he would, by his behavior, convince others to make this their irrevocable position?

Did they know that New Hope is communicable, like a disease, and the only way to treat that disease is by evacuation and, then, systematic leveling to rubble?

Did they know that time was against them, reason was against them, and the hopes of good people everywhere were against them?

Did they know that their data were manufactured, with a probable error as large as the range—therefore, both dishonest and error-ridden? Totally unusable for other than useless or malevolent intents?

Did they know that there were people—influential people—who thought of them and their associates in most unflattering ways?

Did they know about such people as Jean Vanier and the movement of L'Arche—the Arch—which he built and sustains, and Daybreak, the first L'Arche setting in North America? Did they know that Vanier has created places for the so-called retarded and where people visit to have fun, to enjoy? Did they know that the people in Vanier's places were former inmates of state schools—former severely retarded, completely dependent inmates—and they are now functioning, ordinary-looking people, who are valued and appreciated as capable human beings? Did Sam and Chuck know that these inmates could be independent if the state would set them free?

Did they know that, eventually, the Monolith must crumble?

If they knew most of those things, they were only beginning to see what their real public images were—only beginning to see things they should have known long ago. And, who could believe that they would ever learn? Obviously, those who believed in the concept of educability, the revolutionaries.

# Chapter 49

## Purgatory Falling

Governor Majors met with his staff; Commissioner Wiley met with
his. Each relayed the demands of the inmates. It was embarrassing,
almost foolish, to take the idiots seriously—unless you knew better.

Majors and Wiley almost knew better. Their jobs, now, were to
convince their people that this crisis would not merely go away. The
inmates were strong, determined, together; it sounded nuts, but these
idiots were intractable.

> The gov was greatly exercised,
> "I am the chief!"
> That, and a nickel, gives you trouble and a nickel.
> "But, I am the chief!"
> Then, chief, you're in a pickle.
>
> Doctor Mental Health was feeling sick,
> As well he would be feeling.
> For, among the gov and all his men
> There was some malice brewing.
>
> All the groups met again,
> Plotting what to do.
> But, alas, no one knew.
>
> A tisket, a tasket,
> Could it be they're bastards?
>
> Or, merely, incompetents,
> Who have presumed to judge incompetence?

A summit meeting was held on Day Two plus six hours of the revolt. Attending were the Governor, the Speaker of the House, the President of the Senate, the Attorney General, the Secretary for Human Services, the Governor's Appointments Secretary, his secretary (who took the official minutes), the Commissioner of Mental Health, his Deputy, the Assistant to the Deputy, the Superintendent of New Hope, his Assistant Superintendent, the State Executive Director of the Association for Retarded Children, the Association's State President, the President of the State Employees' Association, and some others—deputies and their hangers-on—each attending, each with his own public and private reasons and needs.

> Winter days are short and dark,
>     While their nights are long and cold.
> By six o'clock the world is still,
>     And the people, gray and old.
> The smell of food, and a crackling fire,
>     A glass of Scotch to ease the ire,
> That's what we need to make us calm,
>     A bit of cheer to serve as balm.
> The winter night surrounds the gloom,
>     But we smell a steak outside the room!
> The fire is warm, and we're all right,
>     They can't beat us, not with our might.
> Count them, count each person here,
>     Look around and give a cheer.
> We have the power, and the law,
>     Quick, shut the windows; lock the door.
> No one will ask if we were right.
> No one must know our fright tonight.
> No one will doubt the path we take.
> No one must say we make mistakes.
> The night is long, but not so long,
>     That day will never come.
> The night has hope and fantasies,
>     But dawn precedes the sun.
> The night was long, that winter's time.
>     The food was good; the talk was fine.
> A plan was made, then quickly dropped.
>     But we didn't care; we had the clock.
> Time has a way of slipping by,
>     The seconds tick; the minutes fly.

The dawn is near, yet we're not through.
   I ask again, "What should we do?"
I ask again; you give advice.
   One says that's bad, another nice.
We talk some more, "Hey, that's O.K.,"
   'Til Mr. Cool asks who will pay.
Minutes move, and then the hours.
   "We're running scared." No hearts and flowers.
Hurry, hurry, all my kin,
   Drink the Scotch; don't spill the gin.
Time to vote, this last time.
   You heard the motion; step in line.
I'll call your name; it's yea or nea.
   One last time to have your say.
The votes are in, the ballots cast.
   *The inmates win; it ends at last.*
The fools can go; they leave this noon.
   They'll march together, more toward their doom.
But never fear, philanthropists,
   We will be there while they resist.
And when they fall, and drop aside,
   We will be there to save their hides.
We stand adjourned,
   And pledge dear God,
To save those fools,
   Who know not that,
We are their saviors,
   As You are ours'.
Mid pleasures and palaces though we may roam,
   Be it ever so humble—
There's no place like Rome,
     Belchertown
     Willowbrook
     Pennhurst
       and
     New Hope
Which is no place like home.
And what about Gov Sam and Chuck?
Tomorrow noon they'll have cold duck.
But now there's gloom, inmates amuck.
So eat cold fowl and pray for luck.

# Chapter 50

## Exodus

At noon, on December 14, after three days and five minutes of perhaps the most peaceful revolt known to mankind, the long exodus began.

Subsequent to the decision to free the inmates, Governor Majors, flanked by Commissioner Wiley and Superintendent Lenz, met with the press. By 7:30 A.M., during breakfast coffee or en route to work, much of the nation had learned from Barbara Walters, Tim the newsboy, or the car radio that the inmates had won. But, having limited access to radios and television sets, and with no direct communication with the world outside, the rebels did not learn of the state's capitulation until 8:17 A.M. Mrs. Margaret Swensen, an attendant in North Building—not a rebel but, as she later reported, a sympathizer—heard the news on her car radio while driving to work for the second shift. Hurriedly, she parked her car in the employees' lot, behind the old Administration Building, and walked-ran to North Building. Not realizing she was the only person on the institutional grounds who had already heard the news, Mrs. Swensen was not really prepared to assume responsibility for announcing the victory. But she did.

---

*Word spread from building to building like the certain ripples of ancient tides, like some juicy gossip with malicious intent, or the sounds of bullhorns on a riotous street, but more like crucial messages between lovers, or reports of kings and presidents, or news of great achievements and the telling of heroic victories.*

*Song of Songs*
*Day of Days*
*Super Bowls*
*And Willie Mays*

*Apple Pies*
*Custard Cakes*
*Shining Eyes*
*Clear Green Lakes*

*Thanks, dear God*
*You didn't despair*
*While we forgot*
*That you were there.*

*Thank you brothers*
*Who kept your trust*
*While we were lost*
*Down on our luck*

*Thanks to Him*
*His voice was true*
*Thanks to Him*
*But, thanks to you.*

*And from those who would, those who could prayed:*

*"Thanks God, it was less important what we had thought of Him than what He had thought of us. Thank Him, that the crucial matter wasn't that we had rejected Him but that He didn't forsake us.*

*"He will remember the good deeds of these inmates and their comrades. He may bless them, and their children, and their children's children, for their faithfulness, for helping Him to set the slaves free, for helping Him deliver His people from bondage, for helping Him show this world what it may become."*

---

There was work to be done and little time—but enough. The exodus had been planned for many weeks, and each person knew his role and responsibilities. By 9:30 A.M. of that fateful day, inmates and collaborators had eaten their first meals in almost three days. There was little loud shouting, no grabbing for food or drink, no locker-room fun. Reactions to the state's capitulation ranged from smiles, a few epithets, to some laughter and a little boasting. A few people formed to pray together, informally, but with some in unison.

At 11:00 A.M., all personal belongings were packed. Each group leader had already inspected the situation, had estimated possible problems, reviewed the sick and the infirm for whom he must provide, and estimated what was still needed to permit the journey. For example, a crutch had yet to be found for an inmate in West Building, Marie Pascalli, age thirty-seven. She had been waiting eight weeks for a replacement for the crutch lost, or stolen, during the Columbus Day parade. William Dinger, age fifty-seven, had to have a refill of Dilantin, his anticonvulsant drug. The institutional pharmacy's supply was depleted—had been for more than a week—so an inmate, now ex-inmate, was dispatched by car to the town of New Hope, to Anderson's Drug Store, to fill Mr. Dinger's prescription. Thus, Armand Oster was the first freed man to leave the institution. He purchased the drug, using the prescription written by Dr. Ted Goodman and paying for it with a hurried collection taken up in Fernald Hall.

Those ambulatory rebels who could make decisions and assume responsibility had been assigned to lead groups. People who needed regular supervision or support were also assigned, as were those on crutches, those with braces, those in wheelchairs, and those bedfast. All such decisions had been made days earlier, but now each was double-checked by group leaders and then reported to the Coordinating Committee, where last-minute changes could be made, where any new plans or tactical shifts could be presented and discussed.

Ex-inmates too weak, too sick, or too "out of it" were each assigned a helper. It was the helper's job to audit and then provide those considerations required by the ex-inmate to permit him to join the exodus. The final special equipment and supplies count included:

107 wheelchairs (four of these motorized)
 54 pair of crutches
 43 canes
126 stretchers (each requiring two bearers)
214 assorted limb braces and various other prostheses
184 pounds of drugs
234 pounds of other medical supplies

General equipment and supplies included:

 73 automobiles
  3 trucks
  4 motorcycles
14,200 pounds of food
 3,450 blankets, including 297 sleeping bags
12,875 pounds of clothing, including shoes
 83 Coleman-type stoves and hot plates
 16 large tents
 33 small tents
    assorted utensils, transistor radios, toilet
    articles, and books, including 714 Bibles.

None of the equipment, supplies, or clothing was state-issued or owned. All the clothing was either owned by members of the group or donated during the preparation phase. Similarly, the wheelchairs, crutches, canes, stretchers, braces, trucks, cars, blankets, and tents were either paid for by third-party medical plans or by families or were donated, loaned, or purchased with funds collected during the preparation phase.

By noontime of December 14, there was $12,457.80 in the group's treasury, a bit more than $5 per ex-inmate. About half of this money came from gifts to the group, the rest from pocket money belonging to the rebels. There remained, in local New Hope banks, approximately $600,000 in inmates' accounts, mostly from unexpended Social Security and other governmental and insurance benefits. However, for two reasons, recovery of those funds was not attempted by the revolt's leaders. First, there was not enough time, and the delay such recovery would entail did not appear wise to the majority of the Coordinating Committee. Second, many leaders felt that the revolt could make it without the immediate utilization of that money, and there would be more time later to recover those additional resources. Besides, a constitution would have to be drawn to guarantee to the ex-inmates their rights and property and, obviously, there was no time for that now; hence, the decision was made to utilize only cash on hand from gifts and whatever pocket money the other participants happened to have.

The overall strategy for the success of the exodus relied on the ability of the group to remain together, in reasonably good spirits and health, for at least two more days. That was when it was hoped— expected, prayed for, fantasized—that homes would be found for each person. How? Where? When? If? If not? Then what? were all questions that participants asked during private moments. However, the Coordinating Committee also discussed these questions publicly and settled on several calculated risks. Some might have said, then, that the calculation of risks was swept aside with large—others might have said "unreal"—doses of faith.

Almost everyone not engaged in the revolt, even most sympathizers, predicted failure and chaos once the actual exodus began. This was what Governor Majors and Commissioner Wiley and the other officers of the commonwealth expected. They counted on the inability of the rebels to be cared for by their organizers, once outside New Hope State School. They expected that, by nightfall, the more capable inmates would return, having had their bellyful of so-called freedom. Concerning the cripple and "incompetent," it remained incomprehensible to anyone outside of the revolution how they were to be cared for, medicated, transported, and sheltered. Frankly, there were those within the group who had their own doubts about the matter. But not the Coordinating Committee.

The Coordinating Committee had a plan that, thus far, was working. Why should it not continue to work? In a person's, or a group's, lifetime, there is a period where truth is revealed, when meaning unfolds, when every decision is the correct one, when heights can be scaled, when wrongs can be righted, when one can achieve what heretofore had eluded him. To a person, the Coordinating Committee now believed that this was their time, that they could not fail, that each was born to participate in this revolt. Even those on the committee who initially engaged themselves with a degree of skepticism were now convinced—partly from their first successes, partly from what each learned in the process—that the revolt would succeed, that it would affect more than New Hope, possibly more than the commonwealth; a few went even further with their optimism.

> Roads opened up from gates of Hell,
>   One leading round a curve.
> And then we saw the old church bell,
>   Waiting to be heard.
> The legions marched away from pain,
>   Past frozen pasture land.
> And, from the sky they saw the rain,
>   Which did not frighten that brave band.
> Step by step, we're pushing on,
>   Away from Hell this army moves.
> I've got this stretcher; hold his arm,
>   Glide her wheelchair; watch that bruise.
> Another mile, or two, or three,
>   It's early yet, old chums.
> There's a clearing past those trees,
>   Beyond the falling sun.
> And then we'll rest.
>   We'll make our camp.
> You're all the best.
>   Each one a champ.

On that sweet first night of freedom, at 5:15 P.M., the army was met by a delegation on State Highway 203, nine miles east of the town of New Hope. Spokesman for the group of eleven men and women who were there to meet them was Mr. Peter Langer, age thirty-seven, married to Lydia, age thirty-two, father of three boys and one daughter, farmer, and fifth-generation son of that land. The others

**216**

included Lydia Langer, Bill and Marcia Kupperman, Douglas and Sari Cramer, Steven and Eleanor Hammerman, Steven's father, David Hammerman, Norma Witenan, and Ethel Draizen.

"Mr. Mack, Mr. Edward, Mr. Schmidt, Mr. Baldwin, gentlemen, we know about your situation. Obviously, we read about it, heard about it on TV, continuously for the past three days. Several of us have visited New Hope State School from time to time, living so close by. We want to help you. Please, our houses are open. Please, let us help."

"You are very kind. Most of our people could make it through the night here. However, some may find it difficult. We will poll our group leaders and pass on your kind invitations for some of our folks to spend the night with you."

"You misunderstand, Mr. Mack. We are extending a genuine— please believe genuine—invitation to those who wish to stay with us for as long as they choose to remain. We will make do in whatever ways are appropriate to accommodate those who wish to share our homes until they can secure more suitable, less crowded, arrangements. You must understand, none of us are doctors and—I don't know how to put this—all we can offer is our hospitality and friendship."

"You put it very well, Mr. Langer. There is no better way to put it."

Later that night, after tents were set up and campfires made, on a large pasture contiguous to Highway 203, the ex-inmates and their collaborators were visited by Mr. and Mrs. Dennis Ferguson, who owned the pasture. They drove their pickup truck to the campgrounds, parked on the south side of the pasture, and walked directly to what was obviously the center of action. They were right on target, for the Fergusons found themselves before the full Coordinating Committee. The first few moments of formal—but polite—introductions were strained, on both sides. The Fergusons were not quite sure what to expect. They had read the papers and observed the exodus on television. They were not even fully sure why they had decided, almost on the spur of the moment, to pack the truck with food, clothing, blankets and firewood when they discovered the campers on their pasture. They were not at all sure how the group would react to this gesture, their attempt to convey a sense of support and encouragement to the ex-inmates. On the other hand, the Coordinating Committee had its own anxieties. What if this reasonable appearing couple ordered them off their land? Probably, they should have asked for permission to camp there. Suppose the police forced them to leave? They did not want to intentionally break any laws. They had been trying very hard not to. But what if the Fergusons ordered them off? There was just no way many of these people could muster the strength to pack up and continue the march without a good rest overnight.

But the Fergusons did not come to challenge, to upset, to present obstacles. They came to offer support and, after this was made clear, anxieties melted all around. In fact, the Fergusons remained in camp throughout the night, first unpacking their contributions, then helping with the sick and the frightened. It was an all-night job.

At dawn the Fergusons were the first to see a contingent of at least fifty people walking from the highway to the campgrounds, carrying large and small packages, dragging other parcels of one kind or another—with one lady leading a milking cow, which the ex-inmates later discovered was one of the prizes of her herd.

The first sweet night of freedom was better than anyone had a right to expect. After initial surveys indicated that there was no necessity for anyone to leave the camp, better judgments on behalf of certain individuals concluded that sixteen ex-inmates might best be accommodated with the Langers and their friends. By 9:15 that morning, after breakfast and cleanup, the exodus reassembled for the continuation of their journey. Noteworthy changes included the addition of twenty-eight men and women, counting the Fergusons, who joined the exodus; and the placement of another thirty-one ex-inmates with families who invited them to be their guests, bringing the total of those who had left to forty-seven, with only 2285 ex-inmates still on the road.

All in all, it was a good day. On toward the town of New Hope.

# Chapter 51

## Declarations, Questions, and Observations

*Adam, you are selling illusion to the once-inmates.*
*    And, if that's all it be, what else is there to buy?*
*But the truth is all we have.*
*    And what does truth add to?*
*At least, it is something to build on.*
*    And why not one's illusion?*
*There's nothing in it!*
*Unless, might you say, one's illusion is that he has truth?*
*    The risks are great.*
*But, are they greater than not taking them?*
*    Fantasy and faith!*
*What else is new?*

*We abhor the irresponsibility of this leaderless mob. We disclaim your legitimacy. We reject your claims and your pronouncements.*

*Would it not have been grand had you but exercised such force, such righteous indignation, such moral strength, when inmates were tortured and ridiculed and unjustly confined?*

*Society must find its ways. The cause for human rights will triumph eventually. Government must be given a proper chance to respond to the needs of the people. Patience! Compromise is less expensive, less dangerous, and easier to sell.*

*But so is ice cream. But we don't need ice cream. We need freedom.*
*Have forbearance!*
*Shouldn't only those who suffer have the right to declare forbearance and a moratorium on justice?*

---

# "Hurried Thoughts and Observations"

It is early into the second day of the exodus. There is exhilaration in the ranks. There is great hope. But there will be stress. A person's strength will be tested before the end. All ex-inmates—all marchers— face tests not hitherto demanded. Not the least of these will be the blandishments to return to the shelter, the seduction (and forgiveness) of the commonwealth; or do these marchers no longer have the option to return? Have they gone beyond the ideational point of no return? Adam will confront some of these matters, and he will be expected to reveal the future, as he had helped his friends escape from the past. But as he worked for the freedom of the others, by the very nature of his involvement, he had to deliberately entrap himself. He who claims to see the apocalypse must face tests that only future events judge.

"Harold Bulger, you not only walk these miles but you practically carry Phil Reich. Yet you never complain, never shout for relief. You must think you're some special sort, Harold. Well, do you know what I think? I think you're super, great, a very special man."

"Adam, I don't know what to say. But now I could walk across the land, carrying two Phils."

Adam, you have a special gift and a special way. Your genius lies in your teaching. As the prophets, you favor people with your physical presence. You favor them with knowledge about themselves. You help them plumb the depths, as they find hidden strengths, resources never known to exist. You teach in special ways and, all the while, you learn as, all the while, you teach.

Adam, you have more than patience. You see through situations and, thus, understand antecedents as well as events. It is not patience you exhibit but, truly, understanding. It is not guessing, or merely hoping, that you rely upon, as you plan ahead. As the scientist, you proceed from cause to effect to consequence, but so naturally, with such grace, that you are thought to walk with a special magic, as did the prophets.

How can ex-inmates think with such clarity and act with such power and wisdom? Sometimes, there are traces, suggestions, of eloquence. So often during this period, there was the capacity for one to communicate deeply with another, for saying exactly the right words at the right time for the perfect reason. How can it be that ex-inmates—essentially illiterate defectives—are capable of reaching for others in ways that even superior people find extraordinarily difficult to achieve?

Or are these passages figments of the writer's delusions? Are these words and conversations tricks spun from the writer's pen? Are they little more than literary license or some special fantasy that the young or crazy always expect will become reality, if one but wishes or prays hard enough?

The writer writes and the reader judges. Which can claim he knows more truth than the other? It should be left just that way; let the writer write and the reader read.

# Chapter 52

## On the Road

The road is wide and stretches long.
Beyond the curve, let's take that look.
Hurry, please, I hear song.
There, see a bird aside that brook?
My heart is full with all these thrills.
The world is good, the people kind.
The earth is clear; it heals my ills.
The land is fresh; it clears my mind.

By noon, the marchers had traveled three and two-tenths miles, had been stopped repeatedly by well-wishers along the road, had been joined by seventy-two people who wanted to do more than wish the ex-inmates well, and had been promised everything from room and board (the best Coordinating Committee estimate was an aggregate of 295 such offers) to the second biggest pig in North America. All of these events were recorded on Leicas, Polaroids, Zeisses, Brownies, Instamatics, TVs, cassettes, tape recorders, you name it. Hour by hour, another newspaperman, another syndicated columnist, another television commentator joined the march.

Things were not working out quite as Governor Majors and Commissioner Wiley predicted. It was now Freedom plus twenty-four hours, and the exodus was gaining strength, not—as had been expected in the state capital—dissipating itself.

It was time to make camp, have lunch, rest, assess the needs and resources. As per the master plan—right on schedule—camp was made at the Old Forge State Park, whose entrance was one-third of a mile off Highway 203. Because of the season, there were neither fees nor park visitors to contend with. However, waiting to greet the group were five rangers (two officially off duty), who not only welcomed them but also offered wood for fires, shelter for those who needed it, and their own strong hands to assist.

The other event that should be noted occurred shortly after all had eaten a very good and refreshing lunch, sometime around 2:15 P.M. A caravan of eleven cars and two ambulances came to the state park. Included in the motorcade were six physicians, nine nurses, and fourteen volunteer aides from the New Hope medical-health community. They offered to provide any medical attention needed by any ex-inmate or other participant. Further, the ambulances were there to transport anyone who needed hospital attention to the New Hope Community Hospital. Lastly, one ambulance was released to travel with the group for as long as they would need it.

Aside from a few sore feet and some minor colds and aches, only two of the group required medical attention: Margaret Dailey, an ex-inmate, who had two seizures during the morning; and Morris Lantzen, a New Hope storekeeper, who was suffering from intestinal discomfort, with a fair degree of regular pain.

When the group reassembled at 3:00 P.M. for continuation of their march, 1990 ex-inmates were joined together with approximately— the committee's best count—325 citizen-colleagues. Those who saw it remarked that it was an astonishing sight to behold.

Some felt that the most encouraging sight was the increasing numbers of parents of the ex-inmates who made contact with their children. And although some came merely to see what was going on, or to say hello and goodbye, 103 journeyed to New Hope to take their children home.

# Chapter 53

## Second Night

*Sweeping, swinging, the joyous sing,*
*Arms embraced, bells faintly ring,*
*Too gray to see a bird swoop by,*
*But there he is, above the rise!*
*And where are we on God's good land?*
*Free at last, this hearty band.*
*Adam, Schmidty, and all the rest,*
*Each one great, each the best.*
*Discard your crepe, your black arm bands,*
*Mourning's ended, we own the land,*
*Funeral over, Kaddish done,*
*The morrow's ours, rain or sun.*
*Death has stopped, at least for now,*
*The devil's fled; we made him cow.*
*We stared the Yahoos through their eyes,*
*.And made them faint; then made them fly.*
*Raise the flag, and start the band,*
*This happy gang will all hold hands,*
*All together, draw the beer,*
*We'll eat good food and drink good cheer.*
*And, by God, we'll have a ball!*

---

8:07 P.M.: My belly's full; the moon is big; the sky is clear; the world is good. Our fire is warm; a banjo strums; the voices echo what I feel inside.

There's a smell in the air, burned wood and good cheer. Optimism, well-being. All is well in the world.

Hey, let's talk, of where we've been, of past travail and earthly sins. C'mon, you blokes, pearls to the swine, cultured or genuine, just don't mark time.

Tell us the stories of your frontier past, but don't give us bull or the usual sass.

We can take your new wine in old bottles, but please, old buddies, no vinegar, no water, no junk, straight stuff. We're free now!

We don't mind—not too much, that is—being screwed. But we want to know with whom we've had the pleasure. We've been had, been jabbed, been reamed, and spleened, dumped on, jumped on, humped on, creamed!

What's left? The psychologists respond, "Only your symptoms." And we say to them, "Not 'your,' 'our.'" And, they say, "O.K., theirs and yours." A guy can't win. He can't be in the game. And, for most of us, we're never even allowed to see the ball park. So tell your stories, friends. Tell of the past. Tell of the tales that preceded this day, that caused this to happen.

"I'm Frieda Perkins, an ex-inmate, now a free human being. When I was a child, many years before most here were even babies, my Mom and Dad left us kids, The state placed us: Danny at the Soldiers' Orphan Home, Marty with the Guildersons, Mary with Aunt Martha, and me at New Hope. I was a good girl, always. No funny stuff, no sex, no stealing, always. When I was fifteen, old Doc Childress had me assigned to his house as a cleaning girl. I cleaned. I watched the kids. I cooked. I learned sex from Jimmy Childress, who is now a doctor at Harvard College. But I always did my job. And I never got mad until that day last July when Doc Childress told that damned committee that I couldn't go on placement till he, not me but he, retired. I remember every word. 'Don't place her in the community now. I retire in three months. Frieda has been with us for twenty-seven years. Goddamn it, let us *keep her* until I retire.'

"And that old bastard—oh, I'm sorry, I shouldn't use that word— old Doc Childress kept me from leaving New Hope because he didn't want to break in a new girl just before he retired. After all I've done for him and the family! I still could cry."

Tell us your stories, but not the ones where blood flows on day-room floors from unattended monthlies. Tell us your stories that describe the pain but not the horror. This is not the time or place for anything but stories that make us remember. And horror will only cause us to forget. Mourning's over; now, we are our destinies.

"I'm Jeff Hubshman. I'm one of forty-seven Jews at New Hope.

Being a Jew is not an essential consideration of my existence. My Jewishness can be discussed only in relation to my supposed defectiveness. For example, one problem I have always had to face is that I am too smart for the Jews at New Hope and too stupid for those outside. For another example, as a child, living in Capitol City with my family and attending the special class for the educable retarded there, I and the other Jewish children in the school were told, more than a few times by more than a few teachers, that the Jews had caused the lowered reputation of the school. For a long while, it was very difficult to understand those comments since there were never more than six Jews attending that school at any time. One day, in a rage about another matter, Miss Higgins explained that comment to me. It was a clear, precise, and thoroughly adequate explanation, and made as much sense as other things in that school. Had the Jews not moved from the Hill neighborhood, they would still be attending the school, and the blacks would not have replaced them and—obviously, then—the school would not have deteriorated. Therefore, Jews caused the problems the school now has.

"When I was fourteen years old, and a pupil in Mr. Carmody's opportunity class—that's the retard class, the class for the mental kids in this school—I was arrested for stealing a car. Two other fellows, Oscar Love and Andrew Horton, were arrested with me. Oscar and Andy were my best friends. They are black; all of my best friends were black, with the exception of Seymour Bernstein, my next-door neighbor. I was committed to New Hope for an indeterminate period. Oscar and Andy were sent to the Boys Training School, a kind of institution for juvenile offenders. They were released after their eighteenth birthdays and, now, each has been through the army and completed college. In fact, Andy has a Ph.D. in educational administration and, I have been told, he is the first black superintendent of schools in the history of Indiana. I have remained in New Hope for twenty-one years. And what was my offense against society? I was one of three fourteen-year-old kids who took a joy ride in a car one spring night. You mentioned that my vocabulary and general ability to express myself is impressive. Well, I have been luckier than most here. I did go to the institutional school, but they really couldn't teach me very much that I didn't already know. Yet, I was still kinda slow. However, just about the time I was finishing up at the schoolhouse—at age seventeen—Mrs. Titterington and Miss Metcalf organized an adult education program for those who wanted to participate. I've been in it ever since, but now I teach—correct!—I teach basic English. And I'm still studying and learning. Now that I'm out of here, I'm going to try to get a custodian's job at the university and attend classes part-time. I want to study sociology, if it's not too late. And I want to live again. It isn't too late for that."

"I'm Adam Mack, and you know my tale. But I've yet to relate what the future holds, where I'll be heading at the end of this road:

"We are a nation that loves and nurtures the young,
    So folks tell us in the songs that are sung.
We are a proud and noble race.
    That's why we hate.
    There's color in one's face.

"We drive too fast, but then we're late,
    Because we're in another haste,
To buy some leisure, find self-repair,
    Weave our hair, seal despair,
    Breathe for health, pollute the air.

"We cannot stop for kindness,
    So he wastes no time with us.
Tarry not, unloved love,
    Break the spirit, crush the dove,
    Turn away from ones you love.

"I saw a man the day I died,
    Look into my open eye.
And, then right through behind my head,
    Behind a head that once was dead,
    Before I fled.

"I ran from a place of dead, dead souls,
    Where too few care and fewer know,
Ran from decay, from sour breath,
    To find freedom again, not official death.
    And, if I'm lucky, I'll die in my bed.

"Out in some field grow carrots and corn,
    Peaches and apples, beautiful lawn.
A chimney is smoking, I want you to know,
    Someday, that's where this Mack will go.
    But, first, we are pledged to continue the show."

---

*And, if they could—then and there—they would celebrate Adam Mack. If they could, and if he would permit it, they would sing what even their silent glances conveyed:*

*Tall and straight,*
*Strong face and mouth,*

*Blue clear eyes,*
*An uncommon, wholly unique manner,*
*Adam, we'll remember you.*

*A careful dress,*
*But rough cut, a working man,*
*Yet very clean,*
*And, in his way, quite elegant,*
*Adam, you'll live past your time.*

*His smell was good,*
*Nothing outside, it would embarrass him,*
*But the smell of the land,*
*Wholesome and clean,*
*Adam, they'll celebrate you.*

*Altogether inscrutable,*
*Yet open to all, receptive,*
*Giving and accepting,*
*Quite the very special man,*
*Adam, who dignifies the human scene.*

---

The stories came from every side, and the banjo played, while our hearts couldn't hide:

Lila Jackson
Age 11
I.Q. 74
Orphan
and
Alone

The wind died down; then the fire roared, as we sang new songs;
And old hymns to the Lord:

William McChessney
Age 47
Committed at birth
         and
In spite of it
         I.Q. 98

Stories were told by worker boys,
As we huddled close around the camp,
And savored these moments of exquisite joy:

Bob MacIntyre
Worker boy: Canteen

told us about the
$70,000
in
Inmate funds—
their money!
used
to
stock the Canteen.

William Strong
Worker boy: Golf Course
Told us about the Club
And the players
And the Department of Mental Health
Who constructed and maintains
the Club
As a therapeutic setting
And as a recreational setting
for the inmates
who
Use it daily
During their work
as caddies
only
as caddies
and
as unpaid caddies

Ken Bucci
Worker boy: Laundry
Told us about
the magnificent new
Laundry
which employs
thirty-four inmates
all unpaid
which he, Ken Bucci, runs
completely
he too, unpaid

And on, and on, these stories were told,
First the guys and then the gals,
Then all their other pals,
Then sleep,

And sweet, sweet dreams,
of tomorrow,
and tomorrow again.
And new hope.

By dawn of the next morning, 1625 ex-inmates remained in camp; 130 of those who left—including Jeff Hubshman—struck out on their own for different points north, south, or other directions. Also, by that new dawn, 650 citizen-colleagues were now members of the march. Four hundred of these each had sufficient resources to commit their homes and families to provide appropriate living accommodations for at least one ex-inmate. A total of 950 ex-inmates and their sponsors would be leaving the march when it reached the town of New Hope, approximately one and a half miles away.

# Chapter 54

## Happiness is a New Hope

What was there before people, before matter, before nothing, before that? What is more bland than ennui, weaker than a lazy whisper? Zero, zilch!

And all the blandness, collective ennui, everything before before nothing, to the X power, added and totaled, would represent the antithesis of the town of New Hope on December 16 at 10:45 A.M.

> We celebrate these marchers for freedom.
> We revel with you in our brotherhood.
> You are heroes, strong men and women.
> You reflect all that is and will be good.

Yet this was the time when small matters, as well as epic events, required description. Without the mundane perspective the story could be told, but it would be distorted. But stated yet another way, without the heroics, it would still retain a special fascination.

New Hope is an old community for that part of America, not old for Boston, Concord, or Old Saybrook, but old for the towns that the children of our frontiersmen lived in. New Hope was settled in 1843 by Amos Langer; his wife Katherine; three sons and their wives and their children; two unmarried sons; one daughter, Kate the youngest; Amos' father, Hosea; Katherine's father, Peter Frankel; Amos's brother, Benjamin and his family of seventeen; and the twenty-three members of the Durkee family, cousins to the Langers.

The Langers originally settled in southeastern Connecticut, arriving from Holland in 1754. In 1807, Hosea and his family and the Durkees, plus four other families, resettled in northwestern Connecticut, on the

New York State border. The country was magnificent, the air pure and invigorating, the mountains majestic. The streams and lakes were abundant with uncountable varieties of fish, and the woods and forests supported every known kind of game. It was God's paradise, and the settlers loved the region but grew to hate the land. It was too rocky, too mountainous; the soil was too thin and too difficult to farm profitably. The winters were harsh and long, and the earth was mean and stingy.

Eventually, with reluctance, with despair, with deep foreboding, after early fall harvest, on September 10, 1843, the Langers and the Durkees gave up their green and white fields—their beloved mountain region—for the necessity of food now and a better future for their children.

Several years before he had married, Amos had gone west—beyond New York State, beyond Pennsylvania—with a group of Mennonites who were resettling. He was hired on as a wagon driver and carpenter. He remained with the Mennonites for three years and, during that period, explored every mountain, every vale, every plain, every forest, and stream in the region, knowing exactly what he was seeking. He returned to New York State shortly after finding the perfect land for a new community, a new hope for his suffering family. This land to the west, he would tell his family after his return, has hills—gentle hills, but hills—and streams, with fish jumping to catch a hook. The weather is perfect, glorious springs—real springs, late falls, time for planting and time to harvest. The land is lush and green, not even enough stones for boundary fences, with the black dirt promising great harvests to all but the very lazy.

Finally, the combination of Amos' tales and their harsh lives wore down resistance to leave what had been home for two generations. The Langers and Durkees left their land in New York State and moved west, coming to the still-unsettled wilderness that was to be their home on November 6, 1843.

The Langers and the Durkees, their families, and their progeny built New Hope. First, there were just a few houses constructed together. It was as in the old countries, with the farmlands radiating outward and surrounding the cluster of tiny homes, together, withstanding the elements and other dangers of man and beast. The farms prospered, and some land just outside the nucleus was sold for stores. The Great War came in '61, and left with the lives of Joshua, Amos' youngest son; Kate's husband, Samuel; seventeen-year-old Joseph, Amos' grandson; and six other members of the community. But the people persevered and grew stronger in sorrow as well as in happiness, with funerals and christenings, in good harvests and poor ones, when the sun shone and in winter's time. Amos grew old, as did his children, and his children's children. And, in time, roads were cut and paved, and horses went their way for cars. The houses became a village, and then a town and, today, though officially still a town, most would say New Hope is a city.

New Hope, population 30,625. New Hope, county seat, pride of the region: university, free library, great community hospital, 7500 children attending its schools, its own civic center, a good art museum, community symphony orchestra, industry, commerce, lush farms, little unemployment, civilization, the good life.

By 12:30 P.M., the residents of New Hope demonstrated that theirs was, truly, a civilized society. If Amos and Katherine and the Durkees could have beheld the events of that morning, they would have felt their lives, their visions to achieve this community, had meaning. It was good that New Hope was created. And Joshua, Samuel, Joseph, and the others who fought for that land would have felt that their sacrifices were not without value.

By 12:30 P.M., the marchers shook hundreds of hands, were recipients of even more numerous large and small gestures of support, understanding, brotherhood. Everyone wanted to backslap, kiss, feed, talk with, offer something to the ex-inmates. Possibly, only those readers who experienced such events as occurred in New York City on that day in August 1945, or in Paris on Liberation Day, or at Mission Control Center when that first module touched the moon will appreciate the spirit of New Hope that day.

By 12:30 P.M., each ex-inmate was safely placed with a family, with an agency, with a commune, or moved on for himself, as an independent citizen with means and objectives.

By 12:30 P.M., the army was now composed of untold numbers of volunteers still in various stages of commitment and zeal, yet no longer with ex-inmates to minister to directly but with many coordinating and follow-up responsibilities requiring attention.

By 12:30 P.M., each of the 2332 ex-inmates was safely out of the storm, at least for that moment, and free at last—at least for that time.

By 12:30 P.M., the world was better than it had been since we were small children. It was a child's world, not because of its naiveté, but for its innocence, goodness, joy, zest, and hope.

Truly, at least on that day, New Hope was aptly named.

# Chapter 55

## Celebrations

Three old men stand on a hill,
Two are noisy, the third still,
"Come back, return, else we will kill."
The other prays for God's good will.

Three old women sit on a stone,
One says "yes," the others "no,"
"When did you come, evil eye?"
"Where you will go?"

Three old men wade in the pool,
One is a goat, another a fool,
The third wets his pants,
Except when it's stool.

Three little crones huddle in a hole,
Two have the scabs, the third a mole,
"Why don't you leave?"
"Where can we go?"

Three and three,
Evil she,
Mad he,
And we?
Three by three,
Shriveled men,
Shrunken hens,
God, what He sees!

The world does not react so one would notice, but reacts inevitably, and not only from decade to decade—or century to century—but from day to day, minute to minute.

And, while New Hope celebrated, the earth watched and reacted. What was cause and what was effect? What comes first, scrambled eggs or toast? Were there more important observations to record than those now presented? Certainly, but our spotlight was on these places. Who is unlike the proverbial fellow who searched one evening for his lost watch under a lamp post? Are we any brighter or better than that man who, when asked where he lost the watch, said, "Down the street."

"Then why search for it under this lamp post?"

"Why? This is the only place I can search. There's a light here, and it is dark there."

Each of us has his own real or ideational lights. Mine were focused on a number of events during that period and the following represents but one perspective, mine. It must also be mentioned that these events are not in any causal, chronological, or even logical sequence.

In Waltham, Massachusetts, Gunnar Dybwad placed a call to Wolf Wolfensberger, finally tracking him down in St. Louis, at 2:00 A.M. Central Standard Time—which, incidentally, was not an unusual time for that wild Norwegian to place a call.

"Wolf, did you hear the good news from New Hope?"

"Yes, but is anything wrong?"

"No, everything is wonderful. Goodbye!"

Jim Winschel, Pete Knoblock, Dan Sage, Bob Bogdan, Bob Goodfellow, Doug Biklin, and the others at Syracuse University organized a team of student-faculty volunteers to leave immediately for New Hope. They were especially concerned about the children, and hoped that they could help in the beginning period of their public school placements.

At a country place in Palmer, Massachusetts, five students from the University of Massachusetts—volunteers who had just finished a work assignment at Belchertown State School—sat around a rough oak table. Basking in the warmth of their thoughts, feeling good—"hopeful" is a better word—about events west, they created some verse that they hoped would memorialize that day for them:

> In that place lived 2000 souls,
> Some were naked; some were clothed,
> A few stayed warm, too many cold,
> The live were dead; the young died old.
>
> Three old men sat on a stone,
> One said "yes," the other "no,"
> The third had clout and cast the vote,
> "First you must die; then you can go."
>
> Charlie be nimble; Charlie be slick,
> Skirt the vomit; step over the shit.
> Hold your breath; squeeze your nose,
> Watch the aide with the goddamned hose.

A tisket, a tasket,
C'mon you scruffy bastards,
I saw you leak that yellow stream,
And we ain't got Mr. Clean.

Mucus, mucus freely flows,
A bit of snot that left the nose,
Now it's joined by bits of shit,
Plus orange pus and yellow piss,
Mixed together, there you go!
The bottom line reads, "Old New Hope."

Now there ain't nary a one,
They cleaned it out, went on the run,
Some got lost; most got placed,
Ain't no more a garbage place.

Three old men sit on a stone,
One has a smile, the others a groan,
"Where did all the inmates go?"
Back to life, if you must know.

Charlie planned, then made his move,
Left the group, is on the loose.
Some folks will right their sins.
Dear Lord, watch over them.

Hallelujah and say hello.
Tennesee man's got a new banjo.
The world is good; we're snug in bed.
At last, ol' Charlie's no longer dead.

But, first he died before he left.

And, at the Regency Hyatt House in Atlanta, Georgia, a coalition of psychologists and educators—representing the A.A.M.D.—honored Seymour Sarason, professor of psychology at Yale University. Such singular attention given Sarason was noteworthy—some felt it to be of milestone proportions—in that Sarason is an eminent psychologist who had fled from academic traditional psychology; he is an eminent educator who has no training qua training in education. His only agenda concerns human beings and their development. All the rest—nomenclatures, metaphors, professional preciousness, politics, licensures, role definitions, even awards—he believes are trivial issues.

At the luncheon, at which time Sarason spoke on "Jewishness, Blackishness, and the Nature-Nurture Controversy," Michael Laurence, a long-time colleague and friend, presented him an award, introduced with the following citation.

### Celebration: Seymour B. Sarason

A man is known for his works, and you, Seymour Sarason, are renowned for yours. But you, more than the rest, are also honored for the many colleagues you have encouraged to work on behalf of people, and for the splendor you bring to our lives.

Seymour Sarason, prodigious scholar, truly great teacher, you are a wise and good man. You have taught those who are now, themselves, great professors, yet you must hurry for there is much to learn and comprehend. And you must hurry so there can be time for anyone in need, especially a friend, or a child, or one with a fragile mind or spirit.

Seymour Sarason—author of the classic *Psychological Problems in Mental Deficiency*, the scientific *Anxiety in Elementary School Children*, and the provocative *The Creation of Settings and the Future Societies*, you are author of many books and papers that we, in this generation, will pass on as legacies to our children. In a time not without science, but with little style, in a field where literary talent and academic scholarship are infrequently found together, you remain an unusual exception to the dismal generality. For, is there one in this field—can there be someone? —who dares claim that his scholarship has been unaffected by your unique contributions?

Seymour Sarason, your gifts permit you to record the essence that makes the human spirit unique.

You know ways to teach us how each truth is the wisdom of all of the past and all of the future.

Your acts reveal the depth and strength of all people.

Your life itself symbolizes our human potential.

By your example, we have learned that responsibility to others renews one's life.

And, therefore, we seize responsibility:

> to honor you and, thus, ourselves,
> ot expose your humbleness and increase ours,
> to celebrate your humanity,

And so, to celebrate the humanity of all who would seek to serve another human being.

On behalf of the Psychology and Education Divisions of the American Association on Mental Deficiency, I present you with this award reflecting unbounded esteem and fellowship. And, to our membership, I am proud to present Professor Seymour B. Sarason.

Hugo Moser, of the Massachusetts' Fernald State School, and Frank Garfunkel, of Boston University, were having a drink when they heard the news. Characteristically, Garfunkel's reaction is unprintable.

Fran Kelly, the Mansfield, Connecticut, State School superintendent, took his first drink of hard liquor in twenty years and made a toast on behalf of the revolutionaries. Then, as his staff so instructed, he called Mike Edward to offer 200 staff-accumulated vacation days (including five days of his own) to help the ex-inmates adjust to their newly won freedom.

Bert Schmickel, the former Maryland commissioner, heard the news at his weekly poker game. It so excited him that he finally—finally!—ended an evening of cards as a loser.

A social worker and attendant at the Syracuse State School rumored to everyone within earshot that they heard Director George Buchholtz let slip a four-letter word, he appeared so uncharacteristically uncontained upon hearing the news. But the story must be considered apocryphal. Ted DiBuono, the school's assistant director, was with George at the time and he is willing to certify that George merely said, "shoot," not what the others claimed. We believe Ted!

In Bloomington, Indiana, Sam Guskin and Howard Spicker, upon learning the news, canceled their afternoon colloquium and invited all faculty and students to Mel Semmel's house for a quickly organized party.

George Tarjan called the California Commissioner of Mental Health to remind him of some promises made the previous year. Herb Grossman called George after receiving the news from Mike Begab. From those three, four governors, one semiemployed foundation president, and assorted other dignitaries were contacted to discuss the significance of the New Hope revolution.

While elsewhere a determined group was trying to keep alive the hope and spirit of a coalition of consumers and professionals dedicated to the evacuation of the infamous Brook Island State School. Our observer there reported that, at a policy meeting, one participant said:

"We understand that things can go from better to worse. But who, who with a working mind, can live with the thought that things can go from better to worse to worse to worse to worse to worse. There is no last, ultimate, catastrophe. There is no guarantee that a finite point will be reached—has been reached—and the corner is turned. No one can tell me that this *was* the year of the locusts, that only in the seventh year will bad luck come my way. No one can tell me that, around the bend, there is a solution. No one can tell me that there is always—or ever!— light at the end of the tunnel, or following a black thought. But, this is what life is all about.

"No one can offer guarantees of safety. No one should expect a predictable future. Living is for those who will risk the idea of living. Living is for those who will grasp this time to do something, to feel alive.

"And those who are bloodied now, those who suffer with the experience, at least we have lived—and we live now.

"Who, what, offers more?"

What can we say to our friends at Brook Island? Maybe it is enough. today, to remind them that we are but the beginning of the exodus; inevitably, their time will come.

> The evacuation of New Hope is not a remedy,
>     merely a step.
> New Hope's demise is not a solution,
>     just an event.
> The death of an institution portends a possible future,
>     but only portends.
> The demise of New Hope was noteworthy.

238

The reality of institutional obsolescence is
 mind-boggling.
Yet, all wars begin somewhere;
A mission must have an initial involvement;
All anxieties are first steps toward freedom.

And we—*we!*—have confronted the Monolith;
And we—who can believe it, *we?*—are free.

My country tizzy,
Once called us crazy,
Of I thee sing.

Of I, not thee,
    or she, or he.
        Me!
        and
Of we—all of us!—thee sing.

I saw the future in my head.
We were alive, no longer dead.
The world seemed good; there was a plan.
The people laughed, and I felt grand.
I couldn't believe that mind's eye view,
So rubbed my eyes and then I knew,
That while I searched within my being,
The past caught up and made the scene.

Wow!
The "when" is now,
That "future," then,
And, it's not the end!
It's not the end.

———————————————

# Chapter 56

## When the World Changed

Morning returns, after dark night's slumber. Morning is here, and the party is over. The parade has gone, but the town remains festive, with debris of joy and spirits of hopefulness.

> From the streets lined with trees
> Where leaves long have fallen
> Little feet run
> Watch the baby there crawlin'
> But mom is nearby
> And so is his dad
> And right by their sides
> Is a tiny dark lad.
>
> A boy from the school, newly in luck
> With a leg in a brace
> Yet a manly young buck
> What a smile on his face!

December is a brutal month; the snows fall hard and the wind tries to hurt. The rain becomes sleet; the sky remains gray, except for the times when it's black. Winter is here and, although Christmas will follow, it too leaves; and all that remains is the bleakness of cold, desolate winter.

Winter in New Hope usually is no different from winter in Des Moines, Syracuse, and a thousand other towns across the land. Winter is mean, pinched, greedy, unkind.

People endure winter for the promise of spring. People abide the darkness to better enjoy the sun when it returns. They do not tear down the barren tree, for they know it will bloom again, in all its majesty—and more. And, each spring, new wonders come. The world smells fresh again. The earth comes alive. The dark and heavy clothes are cleaned and stored. People breathe again. Their skins tingle. Zest returns with the spring, and another new world.

In the year of the revolt chronicled here, winter did not come to New Hope. Fall remained long past its time, and spring came earlier than ever before. There was no winter, at least, so the people claimed.

In that year of the revolt, some citizens of New Hope learned that all human beings are precious, that each human being is entitled to certain benefits—just because he is a human being. These people of New Hope learned that all people are human beings and, consequently, all people are valuable. They learned that each person is given, at some time in his life, opportunities to practice his beliefs about humanity, and those opportunities are, in profound ways, tests of one's own humanity. The people learned that one's life may be enriched as he permits different people to intrude into it, to become a part of it. They learned that no human being need be set apart from others, and learning that was not only good sense, or good humanism, but a way to a good life.

The people of New Hope learned that all each person has are other human beings—that, while each is an island, there are bridges to be crossed and rivers to be forded as each of us seeks his humanity.

> New Hopers, who made some tender dreams begin
>> Unfolded maps of places past, but those to see again
> And melded them with new terrain
>> To mend old lives, relieve the strain.
> First, take a map of dots and lines
>> Note the places and the times
> Cross the spots where tears would flow
>> Mark the days when people glowed.
> Crease the paper along the line
>> Avoid the smudge from all-spilled wine
> And read about the ancient days
>> Of pain, of hunger, of death and hate.
> Then, design a map to show a place
>> For all the people, for all have grace
> That's the map we want to see
>> That's what the earth may someday be.

When fall had left and spring came, 1400 ex-inmates continued to remain with New Hope and other surrounding-area families. Of these, all the preschoolers were either in regular or specially developed programs. All the school-age children were in public school or day care programs. All the adults were involved in some kind of employment, or vocational-training program, or sheltered-workshop experience, or adult-activity program. Those with such severe physical disabilities that they could not attend a community-group program—and these represented but a handful of people—were offered individual help and social experiences in their new homes. The remaining 900 or so were each placed in group homes or halfway homes or hostels. A few needed hospital care, but only temporarily, until their physical conditions stabilized. Then they were placed in some type of community-home setting.

Who paid for these programs? The state, the community, the families, the voluntary groups. And it turned out to be less expensive than state school care. Money was not the most important consideration, but it was illuminating to find that quality support and training can be accomplished in the community, less expensively than in the institution, and more in keeping with the needs and aspirations of human beings.

Further, it was finally learned that the nondisabled, the nonhandicapped, the typical citizen—you and I, your children and mine—are enriched and become stronger human beings from opportunities given us to be involved with the so-called different, with ex-inmates who are now free citizens.

> Mother hens and roosters too,
>     Contain your fears, to yourself be true.
> Send out those young to feel this land.
>     Cut the cord, remove the hand.
> Enrich their lives, and so, too, yours.
>     Don't close the windows; open doors.
> Spread your arms, and feel inside,
>     That goodness lurks, and will not hide.
> See that young man, two yards tall,
>     Straight and strong, a mountain's wall.
> Hear his voice and graceful style,
>     You reared him well, to man from child.
> You taught him right, so we're told,
>     That he owed the earth, but owned his soul.
> And he paid his debts to God and Man,

> When he learned that he, too, once was a stranger,
> In a strange land.

When the people of New Hope learned that lesson, the world changed—at least, for that brief time in that place. But, lest we forget —and how could we?—the Chucks and the Sams and the other institutions remained.

# Chapter 57

## Human Policy and the Skin of Civilization

Went to New Hope a while ago
   And with his eyes
Saw empty buildings, wouldn't you know
   Wondered with surprise

He must have passed the cutoff road
   I'd know it in the night,
And yet he's lost, in empty holes
   Within this vale, amid the light

Went to see the men and gals
   Remembered well, he and I
A few old friends, a few more pals
   This was his life; he lived, he died

Lines in shadows of daytime gone
   Was this his land?
Sorry lights have left the sun
   He wrings his hands

New Hope has died
   He wasn't told
The state had lied
   They all grew cold
He too is old.

It's a new season, and, if fleeting as with other seasons, this one is different. People less often engage in sophistry and academic one-upmanship when they speak of euthanasia, which they now believe is a synonym for murder. People no longer make asinine claims that it is the quality of life that matters, not its mere existence and, therefore, it may be concluded that some inmates are better off dead; some rather conclude that the quality of inmates' lives must be improved.

C'mon fellows, take a ride.
C'mon guys, at my side!
Let's take a run up to the school.
Let's see the dunces, watch them drool.

C'mon men, right here guy,
Wipe the smile, but wink the eye.
Around the road, past the still,
There she sits on a hill.

C'mon pals, ole' sock, ole' boy,
Have some fun, you'll dance with joy.
There she'll be, the New Hope School,
The place of evil, the home for fools.

Almost there, I see the school,
Don't watch your manners, but mind the rules.
We'll have a time in that old place,
Gaze at the peasants, then give them chase.

Here we are, but where are they?
Not in the day room, not in the hay.
No one in those stinking cells,
Aren't there people in this hell?

Where are the old or the young?
No one tied, no one hung?
Don't see a body on the walk,
Is no sound, hear no talk.

Where are you, all you bastards?
Didn't tell, didn't ask us.
Where'd you go, you with no feet?
And what of you, a bitch in heat?

Why'd you leave; why'd ya' hide?
Got ya' balls, found some pride?
Why'n't you tell us, fill us in?
We'll miss the party, miss the sin.

Why'd you leave the good state's fold?
We gave you food; you cost us gold.
Why'd ya' leave us, little boys?

You gave us kicks, gave us joys.
Why'd ya' go, we're all alone?
We can't come here, we don't like home.
Why'd ya' go, we liked ya' so.
Dirty bastards, I might have known.

It's a new season. Professor Ruth Jordan, a black, was invited to a faculty colleague's wedding, and no one mistook her for a cleaning woman having the thrill of a lifetime.

It's a new season. With New Hope out of business, people began to ask what would happen to the ex-inmates. And they learned that *anything* the institution did could be accomplished better and more efficiently in the community. They asked what would happen to the ex-employees. They learned that the attendants found other jobs, some as cottage parents in community hostels. The doctors went back to being doctors, not administrators or disciplinarians. They learned that the competent ex-employees were able to find new, usually better, positions; and the incompetent ones became competent or continued to be incompetent. However, they were now no longer compensated by the state.

They learned that contractors and architects across the state returned to the business of building for human needs—eventually saving the state billions of dollars and returning to the contractors and architects the self-respect most of them once had.

It's a new season. People better understand that all human beings are valuable, and everything else must reflect that belief.

It's just a whole new season. The world has improved for this time in our lives.

# Chapter 58

## Normalization

What is "normalization"? Move over, Wolf Wolfensberger; and you, too, Bengt Nirje; and, even you, the man who may have introduced the term, Bank-Mikkelsen. Move over for Don Heiny, whose pictures tell it all.

Everyone together, repeat after me:

> Normalization simply means making available to the mentally retarded conditions of everyday life which approximate as closely as possible the norms and patterns of the main-streams of society.

O.K., that said it. The words are accurate but the reader strains to comprehend. How can there be a label such as "mentally retarded" applied to a person who is "normalized"? The words are accurate but not "right." They do not illuminate first principles. They do not reveal concepts of freedom, living, opportunity, or the future for a person. Obviously.

But, Heiny's pictures—no, Heiny and his pictures—do communicate. And, we're grateful that this man "followed" a group that remained after the revolt in the town of New Hope, some to work on the farms or in small shops and factories, others to gain employment in the newly organized Citizens' Sheltered Workshop.

Here are the pictures of workshop employees and of a couple from the workshop who married recently. This is what our gang calls "normalization": being free to be normal; being free to work, to plan ahead, to have someone to love; being free to do as one wishes with one's own life.

Gee, but it's cool after leaving that
  "school" working somewhere on your own.
Oh, what a beautiful morning, oh what a
  beautiful day.
We'll dance at your wedding, we'll have a
  wonderful time.
Today, hey?

Obviously.

Here comes the bride
  All dressed in white
And here comes the groom
  Rescued from his doom
Here sit our gang
  Thinking, thinking thanks
And somewhere out there
  The world is now aware.

  Obviously.


Do pictures tell a thousand words? Wrong question. And the right one: Do lives have infinite sides?
  Obviously.

Did this couple live happily ever after? Wrong question. And the right one: Do they live?
  Obviously.

Can we say that their lives are better on the outside? Wrong question. Do they live on the outside?
  Obviously.

Are these not the exceptions to the rule? Wrong question. Were these once the exceptions who are now less exceptional?
  Obviously.

What does it all mean? Wrong question. Is there not a design of things, that permits meaning to unfold for those who would seek it?
  Obviously.

# Chapter 59

## Dialogue

"It's over and we've won. Can you really believe it?"

"Yes, but you know, Professor, we will lose all eventually unless we remember what was won."

"And what was won, Adam?"

"We now talk with each other as free and equal human beings. We won that for both of us."

"That's what we must remember! My options had been constricted because yours were. And while you had few options, my freedom was endangered. That's what relatedness is all about."

"We must design ways for people to remember. But first we must stipulate what is not to be remembered."

"Why is that necessary?"

"Professor, if remembering was as easy as it seems, there would never have been a New Hope. The Bible, the prophets, our own Declaration of Independence and Constitution would have been more than sufficient to guarantee human rights—if merely remembering were enough."

"Then what may interfere with remembering the lessons we learned is the intrusion of unimportant factors that may be substituted for the primary substance, the real purpose, and what was actually accomplished."

"Exactly, and this becomes of even greater significance as later generations seek to understand the revolt. The consequences . . . I begin to sound like a professor."

"Please continue, Adam."

"Well, all I'm trying to say is that the history of this revolt that will be passed on to others must make little consequence of the place or the time or, even, the individuals involved. Much more important are the issues we fought for: the value of each human being and the right of each person to seek and shape his own destiny.

"Anything of depth will be quickly forgotten if people are asked to remember—to worship—places, dates or, even, names. That's why the Fourth of July doesn't cause Americans to reflect on freedom and inalienable rights. For most of us, it's a time for explosions, parades, and hot dogs. Even Christmas Day bears little relationship to Jesus and what he died for. Snowmen, trees, and presents—especially presents—mark that occasion. Name it: Mother's Day, Father's Day, Veteran's Day, on and on one could go. The occasion is observed in some comic, sometimes cruel, caricature of its original celebration. Why? I believe it's because we've sanctified times and places—and people—rather than ideas and ideals, issues, missions. We must remember the substance of this revolt, else we'll be left with little more than tinsel and dead Christmas trees. You and I, and the others, are not very important. We are all being paid for our efforts with the new freedoms each will now enjoy. The place, New Hope, the dates, the details that most historians deify—I know that word, Professor, although I'm still a bit uncomfortable using it—are important facts. But, at best, they serve no greater purpose than to establish a "fix" on the setting. At worst, those details eventually substitute for the issues and values fought for. We can't let that happen. People must remember what must be remembered."

"Adam, you must help us to ensure our remembrance. You should keep us all together, as each now goes his own way to fulfill the remainder of promises made. We must look to you."

"I know, Mike."

"Adam, that's the first time you addressed me using my given name."

"I know that too, Mike. As human beings, we have always been equal. But that was no license to use so familiar a term. But, now, we are brothers."

"Now we know that we are brothers."

# Epilogue

Adam Mack had intended to leave the marchers on the morning of the third day of freedom. He was exhilarated but tired of the responsibilities entailed in not only doing his share of the work but also in continuing in his special role. Several of his close friends had left that morning, one to work on a farm in Todd Hill, another to work at the Dennis Stationery Manufacturing Company in New Hope—a job that was also offered to Adam—another to live and work as an orderly-trainee at New Hope General Hospital.

> A soul bound fast, around a being
>> The ego drips to stay the sting
> The tick-tock heart that tells no time.
>> But lets one know what's his, what's mine.
> Although they see, the eyes don't think
>> As throats alone can hardly speak.
> What to do, last man left
>> Stick it out, or join the claque
> What to do, Adam Mack
>> Play the tool, or lead the pack?

Adam was free, yet he continued to remain frozen to the group. He wanted to leave but knew he had to remain. He also knew that, without his influence, the leadership among the inmates would not have decided to revolt. Therefore, the possibility remained that, without his continuation to the end, ex-inmates would not be "placed" in a thorough and thoughtful manner.

Adam Mack learned his last and most important lesson of the revolt as it neared its successful conclusion. He learned that sacrifice is its own reward. He learned that people who are free do things for themselves, for their own salvations, even though the world may believe that their acts are sacrificial; even though they may be! Adam learned that he had resources and strength—character—never before tested, unused, but still there. He learned that there were people in his world who counted on him, and he felt good about that. He also learned that there were people on whom he could count, and he felt good about that too.

> It's good to feel the way he feels
> He wants to jump and clap his heels.
> One knows the power within the frame
> A sense of zest, a mind's eye game.
> You breathe that air and suck the smell
> Feel so right, you want to yell.
> If they didn't know, they'd say he's high
> Don't bump your head; ahead's the sky.
> He lives on talk, and love, and air
> And, with some luck, he's had his tears.
> The past is gone; it was, not is
> This man reborn, the world is his.

After every inmate was settled, Adam was invited to visit with Mike Edward and his family, where he remained for three days. During that time, they followed up on yet-unresolved problems, met with various supporters who deserved accounts of the results of the revolt, and cleaned up unfinished commitments made by the leadership.

When that work was done, Adam Mack packed his meager belongings, said his good-byes to the Edward family, hopped in Mike's 1968 Karman Ghia, and was driven to the bus stop, where he purchased a ticket to Libertyville, a town 185 miles downstate. Five hours later, Adam Mack presented himself to Mr. Joseph Galvan, Personnel Officer of the Libertyville State School. He claimed to have substantial experience and was seeking a position as an attendant, grade II.

By 4:00 P.M., Adam Mack was a state employee, working the third shift in Dayton Hall, a dormitory for 138 severely mentally retarded ambulatory males.

> On this day, he reinherits the earth
>   A feast day, a day to celebrate.
> On this day, he is reborn
>   A one-of-a-kind, with never a kind like it, day.
> On this day, meanness submerges

And pimps die of embarrassment.
On this day, Adam finds hidden resources
And those are but beginnings.
Not an end
   But a start
Not the conclusion
   But the premise
Not the analysis
   But the synthesis
Not the goal
   But the process.
That, Adam discovers
As he searches for new meanings
For new conceptions
New strengths
New visions
An unfolding future.
That holds nothing but good
For him who would confront it.

Someday, someone may ask, "Was there a man called Adam Mack? I know the story, but did it really happen? It is hardly believable."

And, an old-timer, one who first heard it as news, not as history— an old-timer who had been away for many years, far away in some secluded place—may reassure the younger person that it surely did happen and he, too, was astonished that mentally defective inmates were capable of leading a revolt.

"No, no, that isn't what's unbelievable. That's entirely to be expected. What astonishes me is why a supposedly civilized society permitted the existence of such abominations as New Hope and those other places. That's the incredible part of the story. That's the part I find difficult to accept as other than the exercise of an author's license to create a story atmosphere."

Then, another old-timer, one who actually lived through those days as a participant—an ex-inmate, maybe now a retired factory worker— may relate the events as they actually occurred.

"Adam Mack was Moses to our people. He saw terrible things, heard horrible voices, stood as witness to the mocking and degradation of his brothers and sisters, until everything he had was gone, except a sense of his own goodness. And, when that sense of goodness fought to leave him, to strip him bare as the others were stripped, to turn him as it turned the others away from the human family, he said, 'No! You have taken enough. There will be no more deceit, no more cruelty, no more inhumanity. I will leave this place, and so will all people who want more than what the commonwealth would offer a human being.' "

Once I thought that the most unusual fact concerning my participation in the revolt was that I never lost even part of a night's sleep during all of those months, including the time between December 11 and 16. My diary remained important to me, but not very unusual. I now feel somewhat differently. And, with the entries of my last days at Libertyville—but that's another story—I become more and more uncertain about what will lead to what, and who will lead from wherever. Maybe I'm deluding myself, but I think—at least, today— that there are people somewhere who could become more interested in separating the ideology of this movement from the habits—or even achievements—of its participants.

At least, today, I have hopes for the substance, if not all of the words, of my diary and this story I was persuaded to write. There is little more to say, except that once I was innocent and, during that time, I decided to become a writer. And I may have written this book because one who has seen these troubles needs something to escape into.

May 23, 1975

Revolt of the Idiots is a novel that describes a peaceful but dramatic revolution by the inmates of an upstate New York institution for the retarded. The revolt was led by an inmate whose IQ was "normal." However, early in life, he was labeled as being retarded.

The hero reached his middle twenties with this label, but he realized that he was different from most of the others. With the assistance of a university professor and others, he successfully planned and managed a "revolt" that helped the inmates to escape from the institution. It could happen. It should happen.